For **thin** card you can use old
christmas cards, stiffeners from
new shirts or
food boxes.

CARD

For **thick**
card - something
like a shoe box or
big box.

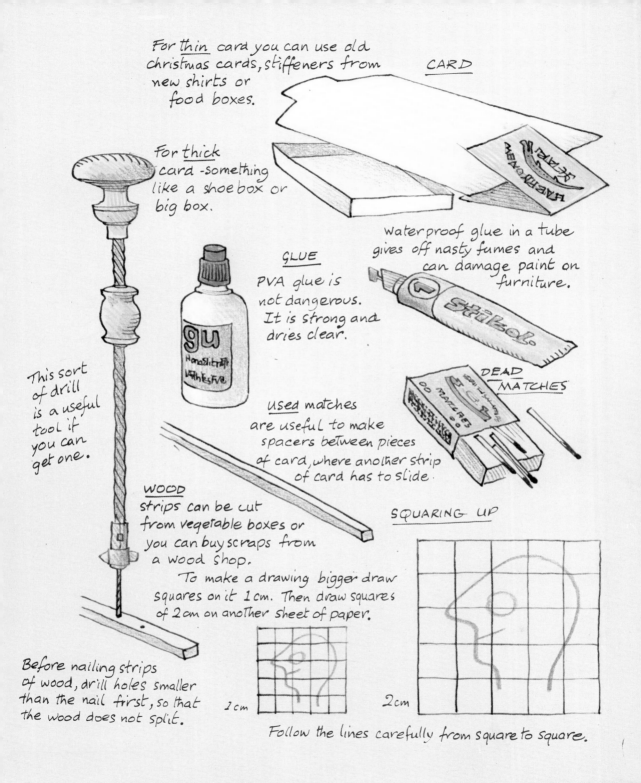

Waterproof glue in a tube
gives off nasty fumes and
can damage paint on
furniture.

GLUE

PVA glue is
not dangerous.
It is strong and
dries clear.

This sort
of drill
is a useful
tool if
you can
get one.

DEAD
MATCHES

Used matches
are useful to make
spacers between pieces
of card, where another strip
of card has to slide.

WOOD
strips can be cut
from vegetable boxes or
you can buy scraps from
a wood shop.

SQUARING UP

To make a drawing bigger draw
squares on it 1 cm. Then draw squares
of 2 cm on another sheet of paper.

Before nailing strips
of wood, drill holes smaller
than the nail first, so that
the wood does not split.

1cm

2cm

Follow the lines carefully from square to square.

Tricks & Tales

Kaye & Ward

Published by Kaye & Ward Ltd
The Windmill Press
Kingswood, Tadworth, Surrey
1982

ISBN 0 7182 2600 3

Composition in Palatino by
Filmtype Services Limited,
Scarborough, North Yorkshire

Printed in Great Britain by
William Clowes (Beccles) Ltd,
Beccles and London

For Rachel and Ross
and everyone else

PETER FIRMIN

Tricks & Tales

Some stories told by the
artist to his young friends,
with puppets and paper
toys to make, and simple
ways to bring pictures to life

CONTENTS

Stories

Real Gold	15
Tidy Mice	28
The Stone	36
Hole in the Sky	48
Dry Rot	56
The Starling	68
Jack's Flowers	81
Moving Mole	95
The Troll	107
Bedtime Story	120
Low Cloud	130

Nature's Tricks

Tortoiseshell Butterfly	22
Animal Tricks	42
Mimics	74
Water Tricks	114

Moving Pictures

A Walking Caterpillar	26
Running Squirrel	46
Swimming Frog	62
Two Snakes	64
Paddle Steamer	92

Puppets

Finger Mice	35
A Fox Glove Puppet	44
Owl Glove Puppet	54
Punk Hippo	66
A Birds' Nest	78
A Simple Troll	118
Sitting - Bear	128
The Artist	138

Paper Toys

Flutterby	24
Paper Aeroplane	25
Singing Mouse	34
Paper Star	76
Singing Birds	77
Paper cup	117
A Pop-up house	126

Toys

Swinging Sailor	89
Jack-in-a-Box	90
Parky's Meter	102
Moving Mole	104
The Octopus	116

The Studio

In the Artist's Studio there is a big leather armchair. It is very old and worn, with sagging springs and loose buttons and the ends of the arms have a kind of cross-eyed look. But it's very comfortable; just the sort of armchair to snuggle down into while listening to a story. It is a very special armchair.

It is kept especially for the Artist's young friends. If the Artist is busy they can sit there and watch. They don't get in his way a bit, and if they are lucky he might tell them a story while he works or even show them how to make a picture move or a simple puppet.

This book has some of the stories in it and shows how to make some puppets and pictures and how to do a few simple tricks.

1. Real Gold

It was a warm day in June. The hay had been cut and the sun had dried it so that it could be turned and baled.

The Artist could see across the river to where the bales were being stacked ready to be collected by the farm trailer. This was a job that the children liked to help with. When all the bales had been stacked they sometimes came to play in the fields. They would pretend that the tall heaps of bales were castles or red indian stockades.

But it was extra hot today. Too hot to play "King of the Castle" or "Cowboys and Indians". It was a day for the river.

Just opposite the Artist's studio was a shallow place where the banks sloped down to the water. The sandy ground made a sort of beach where even the smallest child could paddle safely.

The Artist watched two girls and a boy run down to the river, fling off their shoes and socks, and splash into the water.

'Ooh! It's cold,' shouted the smallest girl, 'but it's lovely.'

'Just what I needed,' said the boy.

'The water weeds tickle my toes,' giggled the other girl.

They waded out across the river to where the Artist was sitting. The water was very low in the summer. It didn't even come up to their knees.

15

'Hello!' called the Artist. 'That looks cool. Mind if I join you?'

'Come on in,' they said. 'The water's lovely.'

The Artist took off his shoes and waded in.

'Very nice,' he said, shivering, 'but I know another way to keep cool. Anyone for lemonade?'

He climbed out onto the grass.

'Come on then,' he said.

'I didn't bring a towel,' wailed the little girl whose name was Alison. 'My feet are all wet!'

'Yes, they would be,' said the Artist. 'I'll find you some towels, Alison.' He always remembered names. 'You too, Katy and Tom; come in and dry yourselves and I'll fetch the lemonade from the fridge.'

So the Artist fetched towels, Katy carried the lemonade and Tom took the glasses into the studio.

'Tell us a story,' said Alison . . . 'Please.'

'What sort of story would you like?' asked the Artist.

'A magic story,' said Tom.

'A story about gold,' said Alison.

'I would like a real story,' said Katy, who was a very sensible girl. 'A story about things that really truly happen.'

'Well, settle yourselves into the big armchair and I'll try to please you all,' said the Artist. 'It will be a bit of a squeeze, but you can sit on the arms, I don't mind.'

'This is a story about a Queen who loved gold,' began the Artist. 'She knew that once upon a time there was a King who could turn anything into gold just by touching it. She wanted to find out how it was done. Mind you, she was very rich already. She had one of everything in the world and two of some things. And everything she had, from her horses and carriages right down to the knives and forks in the royal kitchens were the best that money could buy. So you see, she didn't really need gold.

It was just that once she heard that ordinary things could be turned into

16

travelling along the road without horses! A man could sit on his machine and by pushing hard on the foot pedals, he could travel at almost TEN miles an hour! They called it a 'bicycle' and it was very dangerous!

The inventors trembled with fear as they stood before the Queen.

"I wish to know," she said, "how to turn things into gold."

"Gold?" said the inventors. They looked at each other and shook their heads. "It can't be done."

"You can make machines, can't you," said the Queen. "You're supposed to be clever inventors. Make a machine to turn things into gold. I'll give you a week."

She was impatient as well as greedy.

So the inventors made machines.

They spun wires and heated iron bars. They stretched copper tubes and hammered brass sheets. But their machines could not turn anything into gold.

"It's impossible," said the inventors.

The Queen became very angry and red in the face.

"Put them in prison!" she ordered.

The Queen sent for her scientists.

Now, the scientists were very clever. They were always mixing things in glass jars and boiling up liquids in big pots. They made fireworks and foul smells. They made creams for corns and powders for pimples. They even discovered a new way to make sparks like lightning, with coils of

gold she had to know how to do it. She thought it would be wonderful to have golden plates, golden horses or even a golden castle!

She was very greedy!

So she sent for her inventors.

Now her inventors were very clever. They had made machines for catching the wind. They called them 'windmills'. They had made great collectors for storing the heat of the sun.

They had even made a machine for

wire and bars of iron. It was very pretty but not very useful. They called it electricity and it was very dangerous!

The scientists stood before the Queen.

"You must find a way," she said, "to turn ordinary things into gold."

"Gold?" repeated the scientists. "It might be possible."

"Go and do it then," ordered the Queen. "You've got a week."

"Too short," said the scientists. "We'll need longer than that."

"Well I'll give you seven days."

She was crafty as well as impatient and greedy.

So the scientists set up their bottles and tubes. They mixed acids and powders. They made lots of coloured smoke and shiny bubbles but they did not make gold.

The Queen became angrier and her nose became red.

"Throw them in with the inventors!" she said.

The Queen sent for her magicians.

Now the magicians were very, very clever. They could do a few card tricks and that sort of thing but they couldn't really do any magic. But they were so clever that nobody had ever found out.

"You must make spells," said the Queen, "to turn things into gold."

"Gold?" said the magicians. "Of course we will, your Majesty."

"And no tricks," said the Queen. "Everything will be tested by the royal goldsmith."

She was cunning as well as crafty and impatient and greedy.

So the magicians got out their magic books and read out strange spells. They waved their wands over brass pots and copper kettles but their hearts were not in it because they knew very well that they couldn't really turn anything into anything else, least of all gold.

When they asked the Queen to pick a card, hoping she would forget the gold, she became so angry that her ears turned red.

"Fling them in with the others!" she said.

So there they were.

The inventors and the scientists and the magicians, all in prison. They argued about making gold. They shouted and quarrelled. They made so much noise that the prison warder got a very bad headache.

He sent for his son Timothy.

"Take my warder's whistle and the keys," he said. "Look after the prison for a few minutes."

And he staggered out with his hands over his ears to get some aspirins for his headache.

So Timothy was left alone with all the noisy prisoners. For a little while he listened to all the shouting. Then he put the warders whistle to his lips and blew as hard as he could.

The shouting stopped.

The prisoners stared.

"This morning," said Timothy, "I saw something turn into gold!"

"What?" "Where?" "How?" "When?" All the old men started to shout together.

Timothy blew on his whistle again.

The men stopped shouting, the door flew open, and in rushed the warder and the Queen.

"Here, here!" said the warder, "What's going on?"

"He says he saw something turn into gold," said one of the prisoners.

"Tell me, tell me," said the Queen.

Timothy put a jam jar on the table. Hanging inside was a golden spiky thing. Not glittery gold like a polished brass ornament but glowing rich like real gold.

"Last week," said Timothy, "This was just a yellow and black caterpillar. This morning it had turned into a golden chrysalis, and soon it will become a butterfly!"

"Beautiful!" said the Queen.

"How inventive!" said the inventors.

"Intriguing!" said the scientists.

"Magic!" said the magicians.

Then the Queen told the warder to let the prisoners out to see it too, and they all went out to collect caterpillars.

The Queen, the inventors, the scientists and the magicians became so interested in caterpillars and butterflies that they forgot all about making gold.'

'There,' said the Artist, 'that was a story about gold and magic.'

'But what about the "really, truly" bit?' asked Katy.

'Follow me,' said the Artist, mysteriously. They all trooped out into the garden where some weeds grew behind the shed. The Artist carefully lifted up the leaf of a stinging nettle and showed them the golden chrysalis of a tortoiseshell butterfly hanging there.

'There you are,' he said, 'you can't have anything more "really truly" than that!'

Small Tortoise-shell Butterfly

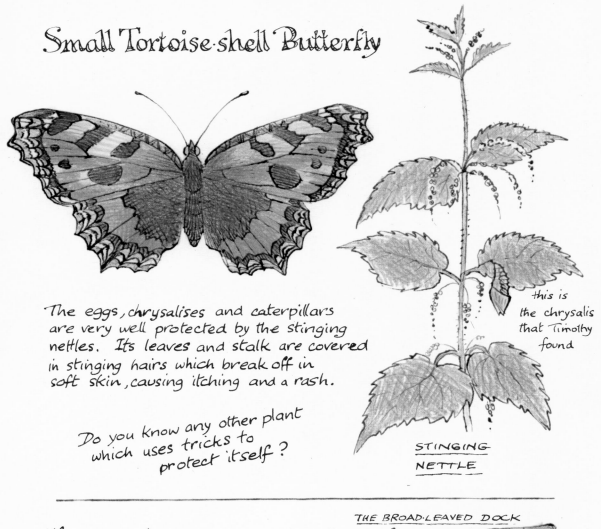

The eggs, chrysalises and caterpillars are very well protected by the stinging nettles. Its leaves and stalk are covered in stinging hairs which break off in soft skin, causing itching and a rash.

Do you know any other plant which uses tricks to protect itself?

this is the chrysalis that Timothy found

STINGING NETTLE

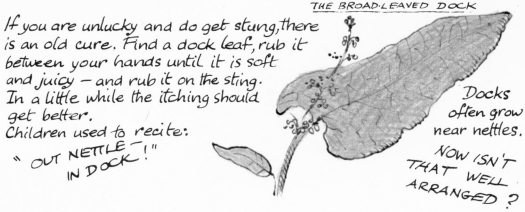

THE BROAD-LEAVED DOCK

If you are unlucky and do get stung, there is an old cure. Find a dock leaf, rub it between your hands until it is soft and juicy — and rub it on the sting. In a little while the itching should get better.
Children used to recite:

" OUT NETTLE—
    IN DOCK !"

Docks often grow near nettles.

NOW ISN'T THAT WELL ARRANGED?

A Year in the Life of a Small Tortoise-shell Butterfly

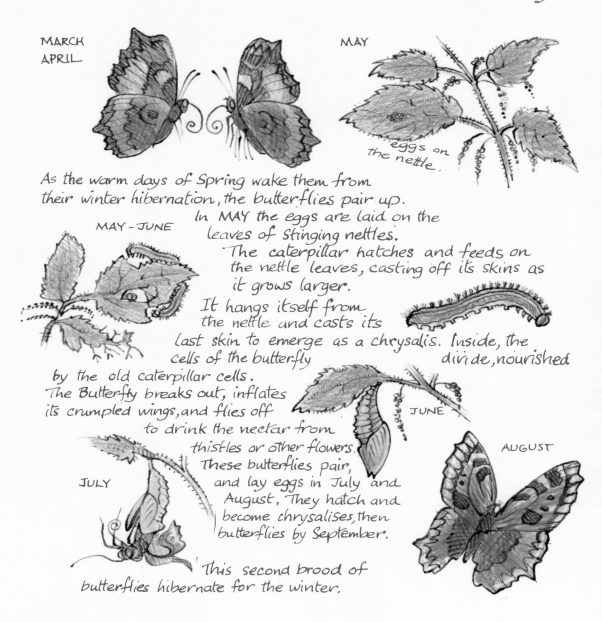

MARCH
APRIL

MAY

eggs on
the nettle.

MAY-JUNE

JUNE

JULY

AUGUST

As the warm days of Spring wake them from their winter hibernation, the butterflies pair up.
In MAY the eggs are laid on the leaves of stinging nettles.
The caterpillar hatches and feeds on the nettle leaves, casting off its skins as it grows larger.
It hangs itself from the nettle and casts its last skin to emerge as a chrysalis. Inside, the cells of the butterfly divide, nourished by the old caterpillar cells.
The Butterfly breaks out, inflates its crumpled wings, and flies off to drink the nectar from thistles or other flowers.
These butterflies pair, and lay eggs in July and August, They hatch and become chrysalises, then butterflies by September.

This second brood of butterflies hibernate for the winter.

Flutterby   a simple string puppet

TOOLS: SCISSORS. MATERIALS: thin card, cotton, 2 curtain rings, plasticine.

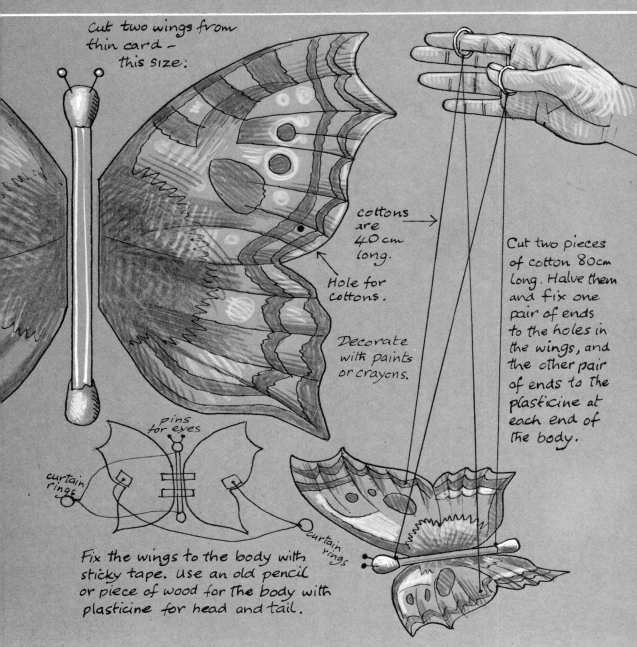

Cut two wings from thin card – this size:

cottons are 40cm long.

Hole for cottons.

Decorate with paints or crayons.

Cut two pieces of cotton 80cm long. Halve them and fix one pair of ends to the holes in the wings, and the other pair of ends to the plasticine at each end of the body.

pins for eyes

curtain rings

curtain rings

Fix the wings to the body with sticky tape. Use an old pencil or piece of wood for the body with plasticine for head and tail.

One to Fly

a paper aeroplane "the original"

one piece of thin paper 22cm x 30cm.

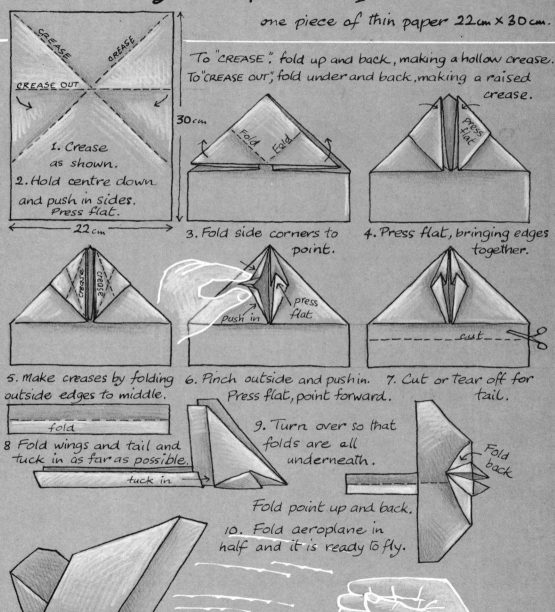

To "CREASE", fold up and back, making a hollow crease. To "CREASE OUT", fold under and back, making a raised crease.

CREASE · CREASE · CREASE OUT

30cm

1. Crease as shown.
2. Hold centre down and push in sides. Press flat.

22 cm

Fold · Fold

Press flat

3. Fold side corners to point.

4. Press flat, bringing edges together.

CREASE · CREASE

push in · press flat

cut

5. Make creases by folding outside edges to middle.

6. Pinch outside and push in. Press flat, point forward.

7. Cut or tear off for tail.

fold

8 Fold wings and tail and tuck in as far as possible.

tuck in

9. Turn over so that folds are all underneath.

Fold back

Fold point up and back.

10. Fold aeroplane in half and it is ready to fly.

A walking Caterpillar *a moving picture*

TOOLS: Scissors, needle. MATERIALS: thin card, matches, strip of wood, string......

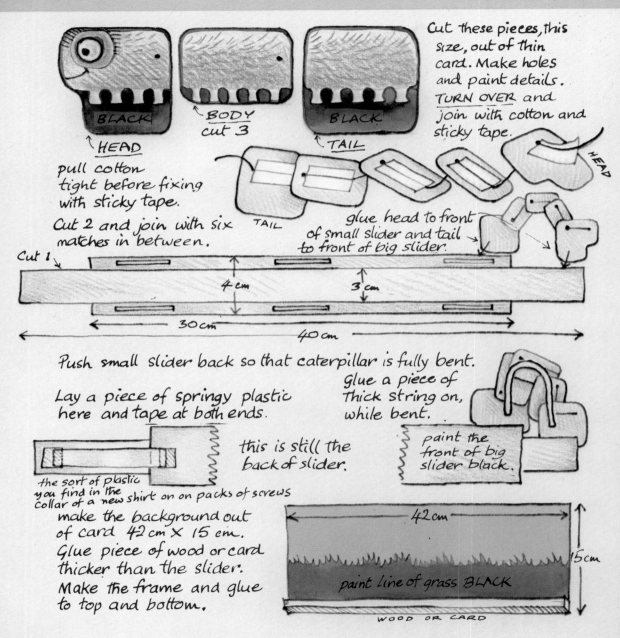

HEAD BLACK

BODY cut 3

TAIL BLACK

Cut these pieces, this size, out of thin card. Make holes and paint details. TURN OVER and join with cotton and sticky tape.

pull cotton tight before fixing with sticky tape.

Cut 2 and join with six matches in between.

TAIL

glue head to front of small slider and tail to front of big slider.

HEAD

Cut 1

4 cm   3 cm

30 cm

40 cm

Push small slider back so that caterpillar is fully bent.

Lay a piece of springy plastic here and tape at both ends.

this is still the back of slider.

Glue a piece of Thick string on, while bent.

the sort of plastic you find in the collar of a new shirt on on packs of screws

paint the front of big slider black.

make the background out of card 42 cm × 15 cm. Glue piece of wood or card thicker than the slider. Make the frame and glue to top and bottom.

42 cm

15 cm

paint line of grass BLACK

WOOD OR CARD

or a Caterpillar puppet

...... old ping-pong ball, furry cloth, cotton, elastic band. glue. springy plastic.

4 cm.
15 cm
5
5 cm
42 cm

OR YOU CAN MAKE THIS ONE. IT IS QUICK TO MAKE AND QUITE REALISTIC

paint or stick on eyes →

Old ping-pong ball

← Glue one end to ball

Cut finger-sized hole.

Pins for feelers

Sew long edges together

CUT THIS PIECE OF FURRY MATERIAL

10 cm

13 cm

Sew in a small elastic band around the tail to make it fit tightly.

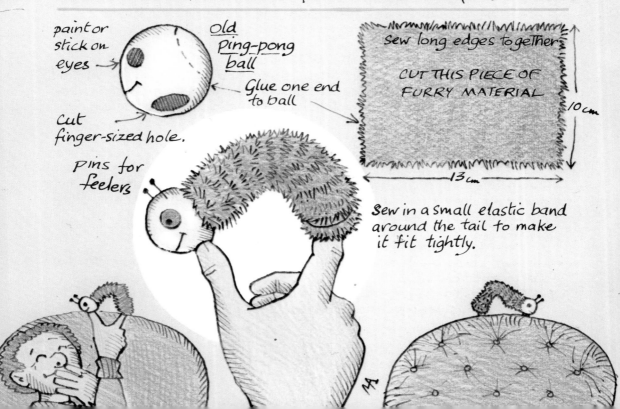

2. Tidy Mice

The Artist carefully washed his brushes and stood them in a jam jar.

He covered his picture with a piece of thin paper and replaced the tops of his tubes of paint.

'You're being very tidy today,' said Susan.

'Well, I do my best,' said the Artist. He looked out of his big bow window down to the river. The sun was setting, the rain had stopped and the dark storm clouds were all edged with gold. Their reflections shimmered in the water.

'Sometimes,' he said, 'when I've finished my day's work and the evening turns out fine, I can't wait to get out along the river. There's so much to see. That's when I'm tempted to just drop everything, leave the dirty brushes and palettes, the tubes of paint . . .' he looked at Susan over his glasses, 'but then I remember the Tidy Mice. We don't want to bother them, do we?'

'The what?' exclaimed Susan.

'The Tidy Mice,' repeated the Artist. 'They're in this picture.'

'Can I see,' asked Susan.

'Well, perhaps I'd better tell you the story first, then you'll know what the picture means.'

'All right, said Susan, squashing herself down tight into the corner of the Artist's big leather armchair, 'I'm listening.'

'The story is really about a writer. He was a very poor writer. I don't mean he couldn't write very well. Not that sort of poor. No, he just wasn't rich.

He was so hard up that he lived in a tiny room up among the water tanks and murmuring pipes in an attic. This attic was at the very top of a tall house in the shabbiest part of town.

Once, long ago, this writer had been very famous. His brain was brimming with ideas and stories, and he had been very successful, but gradually he had run out of ideas.

Now you may think writing stories sounds easy; just sitting down at the typewriter and clattering the keys and watching a new story come out of the machine to make people laugh or cry or just to make people think.

But where do ideas come from?

This writer racked his brain for a new story, but nothing came. Sometimes he thought that the inside of his head must be like an empty dustbin; what ideas were in it had been picked clean like fishbones and searching for stories there was like looking for cornflakes in an empty packet, just a crumb in the corner and that a bit soggy.

Anyhow, this writer sat down to work. He had just spent his last money on writing paper and he knew that unless he wrote a good story by the next day, he would get no more money.

Time after time he began to write but after the first few lines he gave up. The ideas just weren't any good. By the time evening came he was tired and his eyes ached.

The floor was littered with crumpled sheets of paper. He was hungry and thirsty too. He drank the last of a bottle of milk and looked in the larder for something to eat.

He found one cold cooked sausage and a bread roll.

"Hot dog would have been nice," he thought, "but the fire's gone out and I've no money for the meter so I'll have to put up with 'Cold dog' tonight."

He put the sausage in the roll and went wearily back to his armchair to eat it. It was a bit like that armchair you're sitting in, except that it was rather more worn and saggy in the springs. But it was a comfort to the writer. In fact, he was so tired that he fell asleep before he'd finished the food and the end of the sausage and half a roll fell out of his hand among the crumpled papers.

Now, among the rubbly walls of this old house lived many mice. The ones that lived on the first floor with the landlady were very fat; she fed her family on the best meat and vegetables; they had *six* different kinds of breakfast food as well as bacon and eggs. So there were always scraps for those mice, even after the dog had had the pick of them.

On the next floor a business lady lived. She was always in a hurry and her food came out of packets – but she was in such a hurry that there were always bits left in the packets and she never used up stale bread to make bread and butter puddings.

She left the washing-up from breakfast until she came home from work, so the mice on that floor had all day to feed on the scraps. They never went hungry.

On the third floor the old lady and gentleman were not rich, but they had their pension every week and they loved their cat Archibald.

A cat in a house with mice?

They loved Archibald so much that they fed him three times a day! Of course, Archibald became very fat. He was much too lazy to catch mice. Sometimes he fell asleep in front of his feeding bowl and those mice actually helped themselves under his very nose!

But the mice in the attic were hungry. It's a hard life for six mice living with a poor writer who hardly ever drops a crumb.

As you may know, mice are very fond of bread and sausages. When the writer dropped the food among the papers, the delicious smell drifted through a hole in the wall, along behind the skirting-board to the home of six little mice, five brown and one white.

The mice wriggled their noses and twitched their whiskers. They followed the smell to where the writer sat asleep in his chair. They burrowed into the torn-up papers and found the food.

Soon every bit of sausage and every crumb of bread was eaten, and the six little mice, five brown and one white, searched around the room for more.

One brown mouse, a little braver than the rest, actually climbed up onto the writer's lap. She found some crumbs there, in the folds of his shirt. She was so close to his face that she heard the writer dreaming. He was mumbling in his sleep:

"No story – no money, no money – no food – and muddle, muddle everywhere . . ."

Now this little mouse was kind as well as brave. When she heard the writer's words she felt sorry for him. She jumped down among the papers strewn about the floor and called the other mice together.

"The poor writer is having such bad dreams," she said. "He seems to be having trouble with his work."

"Well," said another mouse, "what can we do about it? We can't write his stories for him or feed him. He's a human. He's supposed to be feeding us isn't he? What else are humans for?"

"But he has looked after us and our parents and grandparents in his fortunate days. He can't be blamed if he's had a bit of bad luck lately."

"I agree," said the little white mouse. "It's up to us to do what we can to help. What can we do?"

The mice all looked at the brown mouse. She was clever as well as kind and brave. She looked around the floor.

"Well," she said. "We could clear this up for a start. It can't be easy to work in such a mess. Let's get to work."

So six little mice, five brown and one white, began to tidy. The paper went into the waste-paper basket; the pencils were sharpened (by little sharp teeth) and put back in the pencil box; all the shreds of rubbing-outs were swept off the table into a matchbox and the top was screwed back onto the ink bottle. The little white mouse, who was the very smallest mouse of all, ran in and out

among the works of the typewriter until it was shining clean and the little mouse was not white any more, but rather grey.

As he was finishing he accidentally knocked against the typewriter bell. Ding!

The noise woke the writer, who stared, hardly able to believe his eyes as six little mice, five brown and one off-white, went scampering across the clean tidy room and through the hole in the wall.

For a moment he sat there wondering if he was still dreaming. Then he blinked, smiled, put a fresh piece of paper into his clean typewriter and started to type.

He worked at his tidy desk in the early morning light until breakfast time. He had no breakfast but he was happy now. He had written a story!

He took it straight down to his publisher in the city. The publisher was pleased, gave the writer some money right away, and said he would use the story in the next issue of the magazine that he printed. He even asked the writer for more!

"What's the story called?" said the publisher. "You haven't given it a title."

"I was in such a hurry to bring it," said the writer, "that I forgot all about a title. I'll let you know."

Then the writer went shopping. What do you think was the first thing he bought? Why, he went to the butcher and bought a pound of sausages. Then he went to the baker to get bread. Of course, he was thinking of his friends the mice!'

'Did he think of a title for his story?' said Susan.

'I was coming to that,' said the Artist. 'He thought of it while he was in the baker's shop.

"What would you like?" asked the baker.

"Six loaves please," answered the Writer. "Five brown and one white."

And that's what he called his story.'

Singing Mouse
a paper puppet

dead matchsticks.

TOOLS: Scissors, craft knife. **MATERIALS:** Card, paint, glue, paper fastener.

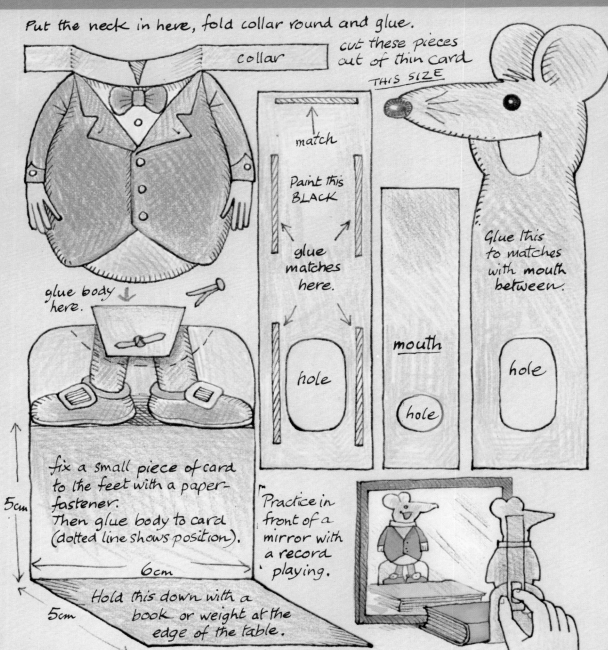

Put the neck in here, fold collar round and glue.

collar

cut these pieces out of thin card

THIS SIZE

match

Paint this BLACK

glue matches here.

hole

mouth

hole

Glue this to matches with mouth between.

hole

glue body here.

fix a small piece of card to the feet with a paper-fastener.
Then glue body to card (dotted line shows position).

5cm

6cm

5cm

Practice in front of a mirror with a record playing.

Hold this down with a book or weight at the edge of the table.

Finger Mice

a handful of puppets

TOOLS: Scissors, needle. **MATERIALS:** Coloured felts, cotton, stuffing, beads.

Trace these shapes on paper, cut them out and pin them to the coloured felt. Cut them out.

ARMS

NECK

BODY

fold this shape into a cone and sew along the straight edge.

Sew head to neck. sew arms on sides.

You can add collars, dresses, pinnies or anything else to make the mice look better.

E

BACK OF HEAD

C   D

HEAD

A

oversew sides together A—B Stuff NOSE. Bring BACK OF HEAD under sew D—A

A

stuff HEAD. sew C—A

B   B

Sew or glue beads for eyes and nose.

what can we use for tails and whiskers?

Make them all different colours!

3. The Stone

The Artist sat at his door with Emma, while the geese trimmed the lawn. They didn't use a lawnmower; they used their beaks.

Geese enjoy a meal of tender new grass and the Artist needed the lawn cutting, so Emma had brought the geese from the farm to have their breakfast.

'I call it "killing two birds with one stone,"' said the Artist.

'Ssh!' whispered Emma. 'Don't let the geese hear you say that. They'll be off up the lane and you'll never get your grass trimmed!'

'What are they frightened of?' asked the Artist. 'I should have thought they were quite safe with you.'

'Oh yes,' said Emma, 'but they are still very nervous. We've had trouble with foxes.'

While the geese nibbled the grass, Emma picked up stones. She knew that the Artist hated stones on the lawn. They got stuck in his lawn mower and blunted the blades.

'Here's a funny one,' she said. It was a large round stone with a hole in the middle.

'That is odd,' said the Artist. 'That stone reminds me of a story about a fox.

The geese flapped their wings. They honked and hissed.

'Now look what you've done,' said Emma.

'Sorry,' said the Artist. 'I didn't mean to say it so loud.'

He spoke to the geese.

'Can't you fly better than a fox?' he asked.

'Honk!' said the geese.

'And you're near the water. Can't you swim better than any fox?'

'Honk-honk!' said the geese.

'So you needn't be so scared, and this story is about a squirrel who outwitted a fox. So you see, foxes aren't always so smart. Come and sit down.'

Emma and her geese gathered round to hear the Artist tell the story of the Stone.

'In the woods,' he began, 'a squirrel was scratching at the roots of a tree. He was hoping to find a few nuts to eat. It was late in the year and he had eaten most of his winter stores – but he thought he might just have missed one or two chestnuts.

37

Well, he dug up a hollow stone, just like this one. He looked at it. He turned it over and looked through it. He licked it and even tried to bite it.

When he'd made quite sure that it was no good to eat he put it down and went back to his digging.

Now, at the other end of the woods lived a fox. Most of the year this fox lived on mice and rabbits. He was very fond of a plump pheasant and if the farmer was foolish enough to leave the doors unlocked he would take the chance and grab himself a chubby chicken or a tender turkey.

He fancied himself, did this fox, and thought himself very clever to outwit the other animals and even the farmer with his gun!

So he expected to make very easy meat of a little skinny squirrel.

The squirrel was so busy looking for something to eat that he didn't notice the sly old fox watching him from behind a holly bush.

"Scratch, scratch," went the squirrel among the dry leaves. And the nearer he got to where the fox was hiding the more the fox's mouth watered!

Suddenly, while the squirrel was looking the other way, the fox pounced. He caught him by the scruff of his neck and although the squirrel wriggled and struggled the fox held

on tight to his dinner.

The squirrel stopped struggling.

He realised that he would have to be really smart to get the better of this wily old fox. He knew that he would have to keep cool.

"Well, I never," he said. "Here I am with this enormous present for you, hardly able to carry it, and you've very kindly come, all the way across the wood to help me."

The fox looked surprised.

"I don't see any present," he said.

"It's a magic stone," said the squirrel. "Put me down and I will show you."

The fox was not going to be fooled that easily.

He put the squirrel down but kept one foot on his bushy tail.

"There's the stone," said the squirrel, "at the foot of that tree."

"But that's not enormous!" growled the fox.

"Ah, no, it doesn't look big," said the squirrel. "It's the magic in the stone that makes it so heavy. But you have to know the secret."

"What secret?" said the fox suspiciously.

The squirrel picked up the stone.

He lowered his voice.

"Inside this stone," he whispered, "I have seen some sheep in a meadow, a cow in the corn and a squirrel up a big oak tree."

"It must be a magic stone," said the fox. "Could I see all these wonderful things in the stone?"

"Why, of course," said the squirrel. "That's why I brought it to you for a present."

He put the stone into the fox's paw.

The fox stared down at it.

"I don't see any sheep or cows," he said, suspiciously. "And there is no squirrel up a big oak tree."

"Ah, but you will, I promise," said the squirrel. "But first you must know the secret of the stone. Come to the edge of the wood."

They walked together, the fox

holding the stone in one paw and the tail of the squirrel in the other, till they came to the edge of the wood.

"Now," said the squirrel. "Hold the stone with both paws."

The fox did as he was told.

"Now hold it close to your eye."

"Which eye?" said the fox. He knew you had to be careful about details with magic.

"Your best eye," answered the squirrel.

"Right," said the fox. "I'm beginning to see something through the hole."

"Now say these magic words," said the squirrel, "and you'll know the secret."

The fox, now careless in his curiosity, did as he was told.

The squirrel said: "Within this magic stone I see . . ."

"Within this magic stone I see," repeated the fox.

The squirrel took three steps backwards and said: "Some sheep in a meadow."

"Some sheep in a meadow," said the fox.

Now the squirrel was near a big oak tree.

"A cow in the corn."

"A cow in the corn," said the fox. "Yes! I can see some sheep and a cow!"

"And a squirrel up a big oak tree," said the squirrel.

"And a squirrel up a big oak tree," repeated the fox. "But I can't see a squirrel up a tree!" he cried.

The squirrel quickly climbed the tree and looked down at the fox.

"Look again, old fox!" he called. "Now do you see a squirrel?"

"Why, so I can!" said the fox in surprise.

Then he realised that he had been tricked.

He looked at the stone in his paw.

"Why," he roared, "it's not magic at all. It's a trick. Just you wait till I get you!"

But the crafty squirrel did not wait. He climbed high up into the top branches and then leaped to the next tree.

The fox took aim and threw the hollow stone after him, but by now the squirrel was out of reach, leaping

from branch to twig, glad to be out of the clutches of that hungry, angry fox.'

The geese struggled up off the grass, chuckling among themselves and went back to their grazing.

'I must get the geese home before it gets dark,' said Emma. 'Thank you for the story.'

'That's all right,' said the Artist. 'Thank your geese for trimming my lawn.'

'They're all the better for it,' said Emma. Then she stopped and looked puzzled.

'I wonder what happened to the stone?'

'I don't know,' said the Artist. 'It could have landed anywhere. Perhaps this is it.'

He gave the stone to Emma, who held it up close to her eye.

I wonder what she saw.

Animal Tricks...

Get-away

The squirrel played a good trick to escape from the fox. Other animals play tricks too. LIZARDS can throw off their tails when attacked, then grow a new one later.

THE SKINK

When this SKINK is young it has a bright blue tail. If it is attacked it throws off the tail — the tail goes on wriggling. The SKINK gets away while the attacker is chasing the bouncing blue tail!

THE SQUID

This has a colour-change trick too. It blows a cloud of 'INK' as a smoke-screen then changes to a paler colour so that it can slip away.

WOODLOUSE
(pill beetle)

The pill beetle rolls itself into a ball. The shell is made of smooth hard plates which protect it.
It is not really a beetle at all, but a crustacean like crabs, prawns and lobsters.

Can you think of any other "Get-Away" tricks?

and Keep away!

THE
ZORILLE

Some animals use smells to keep others away. The most well-known is the Skunk. The Zorille also turns its back on its enemy and raises its hairs and tail.

Then if the attacker is not warned off, the Zorille will squirt nasty-smelling liquid into its face.

Large animals soon learn to recognise the Zorille by its stripes and keep well away. It lives in Africa.

THE PORCUPINE GLOBEFISH.

Normally the porcupine-fish swims along the sea bed with its spines flat.

If it is attacked it sucks in water or air and blows up its body so that the spines stick out.

That makes a very unpleasant meal!

For food it crushes coral or molluscs with its strong jaws.

a fox glove puppet

TOOLS : Scissors and large needle.

1 Cut a piece of felt 5cm x 10cm.

SEW UP

make a tube to fit your first finger.

5cm

oversew edge

NECK

2 Cut two pieces for the body. Oversew the sides together leaving neck and bottom open.

3 Sew tube on top of neck hole.

BODY
cut two

BOTTOM

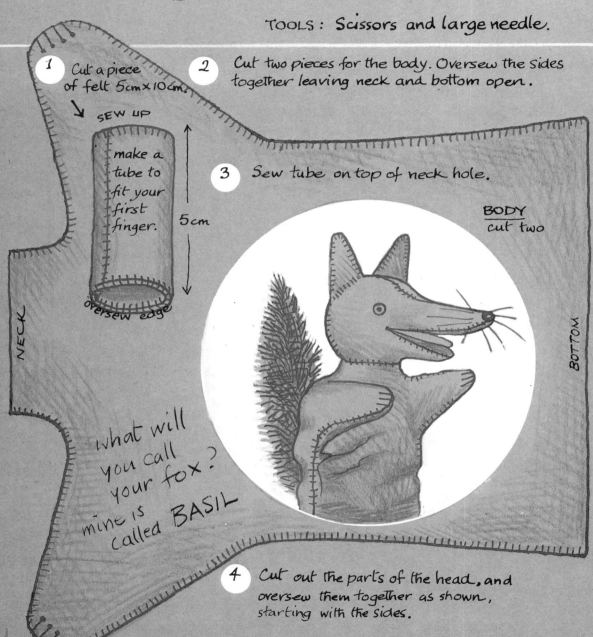

what will you call your fox? mine is called BASIL

4 Cut out the parts of the head, and oversew them together as shown, starting with the sides.

MATERIALS : Brown or orange felt... 30 cm × 30 cm (1 sq ft.) Brown Cotton.
Red felt 5 cm × 2 cm. Furry cloth 15 cm × 5 cm. Stuffing.
Two buttons or beads for eyes. One for nose.

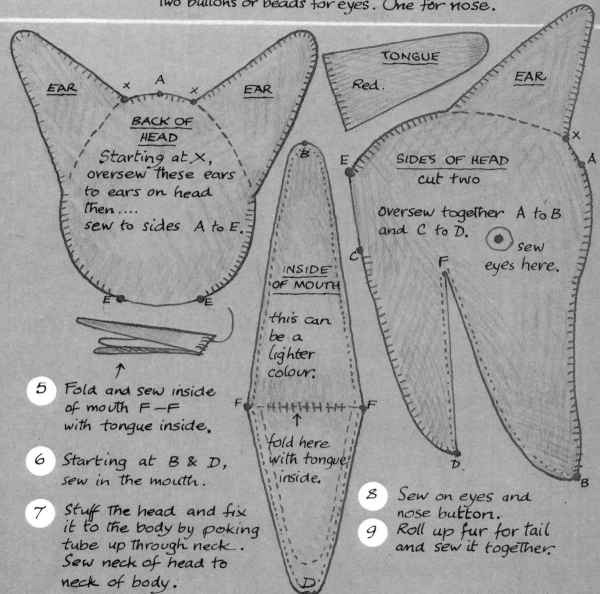

EAR   × A ×   EAR

TONGUE
Red.

EAR

BACK OF HEAD
Starting at X,
oversew these ears
to ears on head
then.....
sew to sides A to E.

B
E

SIDES OF HEAD
cut two

oversew together A to B
and C to D.

X
A

sew
eyes here.

C

F

E   E

F

INSIDE OF MOUTH

this can
be a
lighter
colour.

F |-|+|-|+|-|+|-|+|-| F
↑
fold here
with tongue
inside.

D

B

5 Fold and sew inside
of mouth F—F
with tongue inside.

6 Starting at B & D,
sew in the mouth.

7 Stuff the head and fix
it to the body by poking
tube up through neck.
Sew neck of head to
neck of body.

8 Sew on eyes and
nose button.

9 Roll up fur for tail
and sew it together.

running squirrel

a moving picture ...

TOOLS: Craft knife, scissors, paint brush, ruler, compasses.

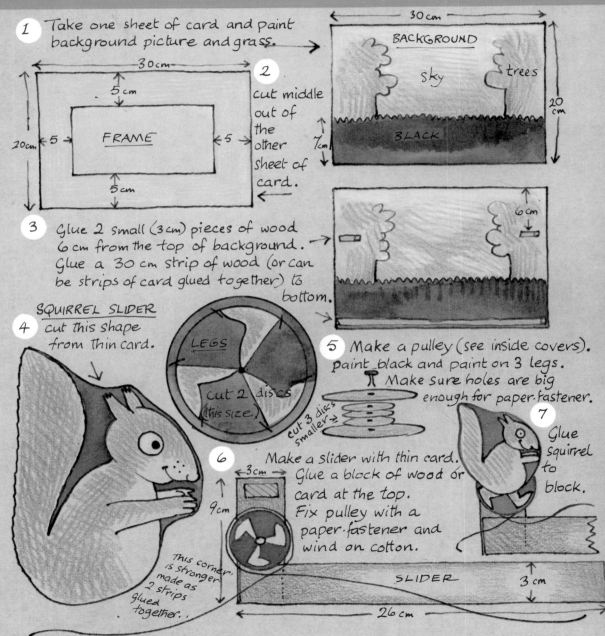

1 Take one sheet of card and paint background picture and grass.

30 cm
5 cm
20cm 5 FRAME 5
5 cm

2 cut middle out of the other sheet of card.

30 cm
BACKGROUND
sky trees
20 cm
7cm BLACK

3 Glue 2 small (3cm) pieces of wood 6 cm from the top of background. Glue a 30 cm strip of wood (or can be strips of card glued together) to bottom.

6 cm

SQUIRREL SLIDER
4 cut this shape from thin card.

LEGS
Cut 2 discs (this size)
cut 3 discs smaller →

5 Make a pulley (see inside covers). paint black and paint on 3 legs. Make sure holes are big enough for paper-fastener.

6 Make a slider with thin card. Glue a block of wood or card at the top. Fix pulley with a paper-fastener and wind on cotton.

3 cm
9 cm

This corner is stronger made as 2 strips glued together.

SLIDER
3 cm
26 cm

7 Glue squirrel to block.

MATERIALS: 2 pieces of thin card 20cm × 30cm, 1 piece 10cm × 26cm.
½ metre embroidery cotton, PVA glue, paper fastener, black paint,
60cm strip of wood or balsa, 1cm × ½cm, Crayons or colours.

8 Lay the squirrel and slider along wood strip.
Take cottons from pulley
through slits cut in background.
Fix at back with sticky tape.
Then glue the frame to
the strips of wood.

Glue
on to
↓ strips
of
wood
and
along the
top.

BACK OF
PICTURE

Fix cotton
with tapes

Pull the slider and see his legs run (Draw in a fox if you like)

4. Hole in the Sky

'Look what I had for my birthday,' said Jim.

'When was your birthday?' asked the Artist.

'Today,' said Mandy, 'and he's eight.'

'That's a good age to be,' said the Artist, 'and I didn't even know. So I'm afraid I didn't get you a present.'

'I did,' said Mandy. 'I gave him a wind-up boat with a driver in it.'

'It goes ever so fast,' said Jim. 'But look what I got from Mum.'

He took out a pair of binoculars. The Artist held them up to his eyes and adjusted them.

'They're very good ones,' he said.

'Yes,' said Jim. 'You can can ships out at sea and birds and trees – oh, a long way away. They seem to be ever so near.'

'Have you tried them at night?' asked the Artist. 'You can see the craters on the moon and ever so many stars. Come outside and see.'

They went out by the back door. It was dark already and a full moon was rising above the trees. They took turns looking at the sky.

'The stars seem to go on for ever,' said Jim.

'You could say that,' said the Artist. 'Although long ago people thought the sky was like a blue lid over the world. They thought there were pinholes in it, and the stars were the light coming through the holes.'

'Good job it isn't like that,' said Mandy. 'Imagine when a space rocket went up . . . Whoosh! . . . Crash! . . . broken lid!'

'There'd be a big hole in the sky then,' laughed Jim.

'There was once,' said the Artist. 'At least that's what the squirrel said. Come inside and I'll tell you about it. I can finish the picture I'm painting at the same time.'

48

So they went into the studio. Mandy and Jim squeezed into the big leather armchair; it was plenty big enough for two, and the Artist went back to his drawing board.

'Once upon a time,' he began, 'a squirrel came running through the woods, crying:

"The sky is falling, the sky is falling!"

'Oh, we know that one,' said Jim. 'It wasn't a squirrel. It was Henny Penny.'

'And it wasn't the sky at all,' said Mandy. 'It was only a nut that fell on her head.'

'That's what the Fox thought,' said the Artist. 'He was wrong too. Just be quiet and listen.'

He went on with the story:

'Once upon a time, a Squirrel came running through the woods crying, "The sky is falling, the sky is falling!"

The Fox was waiting behind a tree as the Squirrel ran past. Out shot a paw and grabbed the Squirrel by his tail.

"Don't give us that old joke," sneered the Fox. "We've heard it before. It's a chestnut!"

"No, no," cried the Squirrel, dangling by his bushy tail, "it's true! The sky really fell. I saw it down by the river."

The Fox dropped the Squirrel.

"Har! Har!" he laughed.

"You don't believe me, do you?" said the Squirrel. "Come and see for yourself."

He led the Fox through the trees towards the river. The path led under an old oak tree. An Owl was sleeping on a low branch.

"The sky is falling, the sky is falling!" cried the Squirrel.

49

The Owl opened one eye, winked and said: "Hallucinations!"

He was rather fond of long words.

"A figment of your fertile imagination!" he said and fell off the branch.

Luckily the Fox caught him and they landed together in the bracken.

The Squirrel helped them up. He hadn't understood a word.

"That may be so," he said. "But I was sitting on the river bank when suddenly there was a big splash!"

"A crow had dropped a walnut in the water," said the Fox.

"No," said the Squirrel. "I looked up to see what had broken, and there was this big hole in the sky!"

The Fox and the Owl followed the Squirrel along the path. They left the wood and came to a brambly bank.

"What's going on?" asked the Badger as they passed.

"The sky is falling. It fell into the river," said the Squirrel.

"What fell in the river?" asked the old Badger, who was rather deaf.

"A piece of the sky," shouted the Squirrel.

"Pieces of pie!" repeated the Badger. "There's no need to shout, you know. I'm not deaf, young man."

And he lumbered after them.

The Squirrel, the Fox, the Owl and the Badger ran along the edge of the cabbage field. A whiskery face with large orange teeth popped up.

"What's up?" said the Coypu. He hurried after the Badger. "Where's everybody going?" he asked.

"Something has fallen in the

river," answered the Badger.

"In the river! In MY river?" exclaimed the Coypu. "What's fallen in my nice clean river?"

"They made a big splash," said the Badger.

"Yes, yes, but what is it? Will it make the water dirty?"

"Pie! Pieces of pie," said the Badger.

"Peccable provender," said the Owl.

"Sounds like a waste of good food," said the Coypu. "Wait for me, I'm coming."

The Fox, the Squirrel, the Owl, the Badger and the Coypu pushed through the reeds towards the river bank. A Coot ran startled out of the reeds.

"Where's the fire?" she squeaked.

"No fire," called the Coypu. "Just meat pies going to waste. Hundreds of them, floating down the river."

"Oh, the poor dears," said the Coot. "I do hope they can swim."

She followed them down to the edge of the water.

The animals gathered on the river bank. The Squirrel who heard the splash; the Fox who didn't believe him: the Owl who thought it was all too simple to be true; the Badger who thought it was pies; the Coypu who was beginning to feel hungry; and the Coot who was happy to find something new to worry about.

"There, you see!" said the Squirrel, pointing up at the sky. "What did I tell you?"

Directly above them was a large black hole!

"Someone's been nibbling the sky!" said the Coypu. "He must have been hungry!"

"Hungary?" said the Badger. "Looks more like France to me!"

"Optical illusion," said the Owl, and fell over backwards.

"Ups-a-daisy!" said the Coot.

"Show me the missing piece," said the Fox. "It's sure to be a nut."

"There it is," said the Squirrel, pointing into the clear water. The river rippled over something at the bottom; something large and blue, with straight edges like a piece of broken glass. Only it wasn't hard like glass. It moved gently with the water like a large piece of blue velvet.

"Looks a bit off to me," said the Badger. "Never seen blue meat pies before."

"The water has made it all soggy," said the Squirrel.

"Can't stand soggy meat pies," said the Coypu.

"They'll catch their death of cold," said the Coot. "Poor dears!"

"NUTS!" said the Fox.

The Owl looked into the water.

"Profoundly soporific," he said, "and Beatrix Potterific." The Owl fell fast asleep.'

52

'Well,' said the Artist. 'That's the end of that story – and I've finished your picture too, Jim.'

'My picture?' said Jim. 'Is that for me?'

'Yes, it's your birthday present from me.'

'Thank you very much,' said Jim. 'But what about the hole in the sky?'

'I've got a hole in my glove,' said Mandy. 'Look, my finger sticks out. I'm going to darn it when I get home. Did somebody darn the hole in the sky?'

'They didn't need to,' said the Artist. 'As the sun set and the sky became darker, the hole didn't show up any more. The piece in the water got darker too.

Next morning was a brand new day. A bright new morning. A new blue sky. Not a cloud – or a hole – in sight.

53

Old Glove Owl an old glove puppet

TOOLS:

SCISSORS

NEEDLE

HEAD
cut two

Sew on beak, eye pieces, eye buttons
and chin piece to one of these pieces.

Then sew two pieces together, except
for neck. Fill with stuffing.

A

BEAK

C

B

make up beak, oversew A-C-B.
fill with stuffing. Sew onto face.

If you have no old glove, make
a body as for the fox on page 44.

CHIN
cut one
sew under beak.

LARGE EYE PIECE
cut two.
cut notches all round edge. sew to face.

C

BEAK

A   B

SMALL EYE PIECE
cut two.
cut notches all round edge. sew to large piece.

USE WHAT
COLOURS YOU
LIKE.

MATERIALS: An old glove: 2 felt squares (21cm) one of them in a colour to match glove. Small pieces of red, orange and yellow felt. Two buttons for eyes. Cotton to match felt.

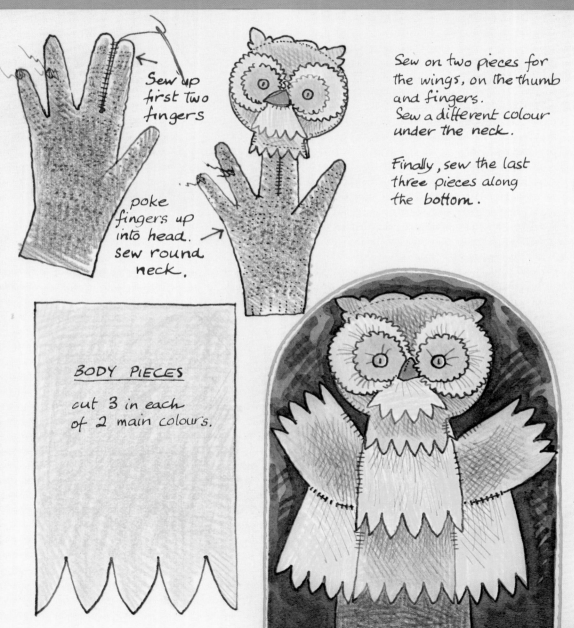

Sew up first two fingers

poke fingers up into head. sew round neck.

Sew on two pieces for the wings, on the thumb and fingers. Sew a different colour under the neck.

Finally, sew the last three pieces along the bottom.

BODY PIECES

cut 3 in each of 2 main colours.

5. Dry Rot

'Horrible rain,' said Henry.

The Artist said nothing. He was too busy painting a picture to notice, although the rain was pouring down the window. It was one of those dull damp days when he liked to stay indoors to write his letters, do some painting or read a book.

Henry, on his way home from school, had come in to shelter until the worst of the shower had passed. But he was bored.

He flipped a stone from a flower pot into the Artist's water jar. A splash fell onto the picture making the paint run.

The Artist looked up surprised.

'It's raining!' he said.

'Yes, and I don't like it,' said Henry. 'I'm fed up with this wet weather.'

'Well, everyone is not like you,' said the Artist. 'I know some creatures who love the wet. The wetter the better, they say.'

'Who?' asked Henry.

'Ducks, for a start; and newts, worms, fish, and frogs, especially frogs. I remember one frog who couldn't bear to be dry. He absolutely hated it!'

He put down his brush and looked out of the window.

'This frog lived in Africa,' he said. 'Near him lived a Pygmy Hippopotamus. That's the smaller sort of hippo; he only weighed five hundred pounds, but he was plenty big enough to make some very large footprints in the mud.

56

These footprints filled with water making big dirty puddles that the frog liked to swim in.

"Squelch, squelch, squelch, squelch," went the hippo as he walked along the river bank. Four fresh swimming pools!

"Plop, plop, plop, plop!" went the frog, as he followed the hippo, jumping from pool to pool.

As the frog plopped, he sang:

"I like a puddle when the rain comes down,
  In I hop, plip, plop, plop.
  'Specially if the water is muddy and brown,
  In I flop, slip, slop, slop."

The hippo got used to having him around, and sometimes even joined in the song with a:

"Bellow, ho, ho!" in his deep voice. They were a happy pair. Hippo enjoyed slurping about in the wet mud and Frog splashed in the muddy puddles.

Sometimes Hippo swam out into the river when a paddle steamer passed. He rolled and splashed to amuse the humans on board.

"Look at the funny hippo!" the mother human said, holding up her baby.

"Odd things, humans," thought Hippo, "with their little round smooth faces. They're a bit like the monkeys in the trees really, except that they don't throw stones at me."

They threw nicer things.

The baby humans would gurgle with delight as he opened his enormous mouth to catch buns and biscuits.

Then the father humans would get out their cameras and take photos of him, as he took up elegant poses on a sand bank. They seemed to like that.

Sometimes Hippo followed the boat almost into the town. He was very interested in the way they lived. He thought that it would be rather smart to live, like them, in a house. He became ambitious.

But the frog was not at all ambitious. He was quite happy to idle his time away in the mud, catching flies all day. He didn't want to change a thing.

"I could be happy like this, for ever and ever and ever," he said.

One day, Hippo came back from a trip downstream, all a-quiver with excitement.

"Frog," he said. "How would you like to be civilized?"

"I don't know," answered the frog. "Does it hurt?"

"No, no, I mean like people. Living in a house, with walls and rooms and all that," said Hippo. "You see, I've found this empty house on the marsh."

"Well, it all depends," said Frog. "Is it damp?"

"Oh, yes," replied Hippo. "You'll love it; not a dry patch in the whole house. It's absolutely soggy!"

They went together to see the old house.

It was in a damp hollow by the river and the damp had crept up the walls. There were patches of mould and clumps of fungus. The tiles were falling off the roof and the woodwork around the windows was rotten and crumbling.

"It does seem nice and damp," said Frog, running his hands over the dripping walls. He slapped and slopped around in the pools of water which lay about the sitting room floor, and tried to make up his mind.

"Well, Hippy, as it's such a nice wet place . . . all right . . . I agree."

So they moved in.

The hippo spent his days clearing out the ditches and throwing the mud up onto the garden. Frog splashed and sang in the wet ditches, fetching in buckets of water to throw on the walls to keep them damp. Then Hippo took up gardening. He found that he could grow water-cress and other tasty water plants. Then, as the ditches drained out the land, he planted cabbages and turnips.

Frog didn't like it when the ditches started to dry out the garden but he didn't like to say anything as the hippo was so happy.

He just stayed indoors in the damp.

Then one day he said to Hippo: "You know, Hippy, I'm worried about the house. I noticed some dry patches on the walls today."

"Never mind," said the hippo, "it may not spread. Even if it does, you shouldn't complain. After all, it's much more civilised to live in a dry house."

"If you say so," said Frog, sadly.

Hippo sang a little "Ho-ho" song and danced a few steps out into the garden.

But the dry did spread. Frog sat all day in the last really damp corner, while Hippo was busy in the garden, and when Frog suggested going back for a holiday by the muddy river, Hippo was horrified.

"You can't go back to that sort of life, now. I wouldn't hear of it. I'm sure you wouldn't like it. Not now you've got used to a house."

"But the house is getting so dry," protested Frog.

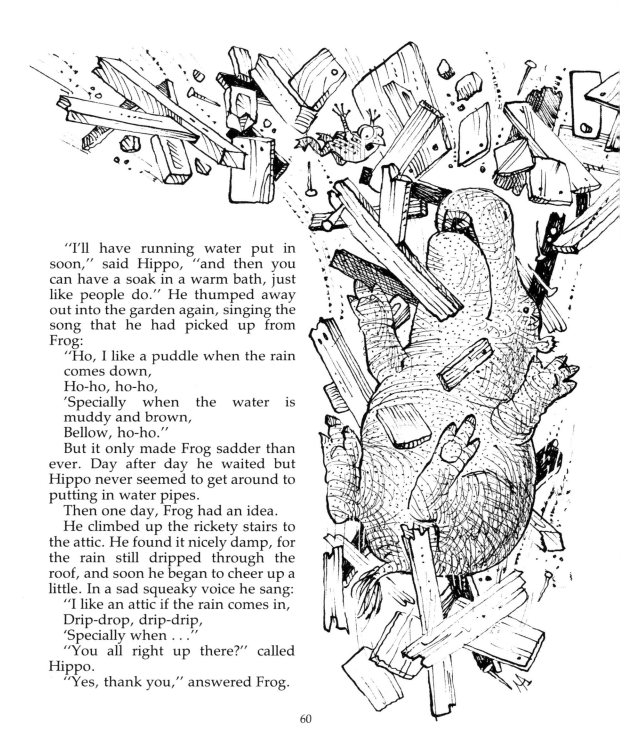

"I'll have running water put in
soon," said Hippo, "and then you
can have a soak in a warm bath, just
like people do." He thumped away
out into the garden again, singing the
song that he had picked up from
Frog:
"Ho, I like a puddle when the rain
comes down,
Ho-ho, ho-ho,
'Specially when the water is
muddy and brown,
Bellow, ho-ho."
But it only made Frog sadder than
ever. Day after day he waited but
Hippo never seemed to get around to
putting in water pipes.
Then one day, Frog had an idea.
He climbed up the rickety stairs to
the attic. He found it nicely damp, for
the rain still dripped through the
roof, and soon he began to cheer up a
little. In a sad squeaky voice he sang:
"I like an attic if the rain comes in,
Drip-drop, drip-drip,
'Specially when . . ."
"You all right up there?" called
Hippo.
"Yes, thank you," answered Frog.

60

The attic shook as Hippo came up to see. Frog heard the thump of Hippo's big feet on the stairs. There was a crumbling of rotten wood and the creaking of planks as he clambered through the tiny attic hatch.

"I got a bit worried when I heard you making those funny noises," he said. "And no wonder, look at the state of this attic. It's terribly damp!"

"But I like it that way," began Frog.

"Nonsense!" rumbled the hippo, and he started to pull his great body through into the attic.

Then, finally, Frog lost his temper. He stamped his tiny foot.

A plank gave way, then the floor started to break up. The stairs collapsed like a pack of cards, the walls caved in and tiles began to clatter down the roof, bringing chimney stack and gutters with them. Hippo and Frog went slithering down amongst broken wood, furniture and bricks, until nothing could be seen except an enormous heap of rubble in a cloud of dust.

When the dust had settled a great shape could be seen lumbering about among the ruins. It was Hippo looking for his little friend Frog.

"Oh, Froggie," he wailed, "now look what you've done. You should never have lost your temper. It's not civilised."

But Frog did not hear. He had hopped away to the river and was happily swimming out into the deep water – and wondering why he had never done so before.'

'So you see,' said the Artist, 'some folks do like it wet. Nobody is the same. Although, I must say, I don't like the rain splashing my pictures.' And he looked straight at Henry.

Swimming Frog

a moving picture

TOOLS: Scissors, craft-knife, needle.

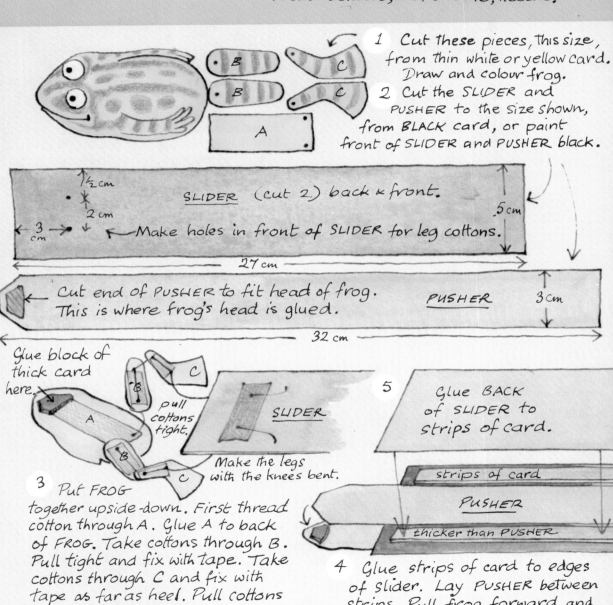

1 Cut these pieces, this size, from thin white or yellow card. Draw and colour frog.

2 Cut the SLIDER and PUSHER to the size shown, from BLACK card, or paint front of SLIDER and PUSHER black.

SLIDER (cut 2) back & front.

½ cm

2 cm

3 cm

Make holes in front of SLIDER for leg cottons.

5 cm

27 cm

Cut end of PUSHER to fit head of frog. This is where frog's head is glued.

PUSHER   3 cm

32 cm

Glue block of thick card here.

pull cottons tight.

SLIDER

Make the legs with the knees bent.

3 Put FROG together upside-down. First thread cotton through A. Glue A to back of FROG. Take cottons through B. Pull tight and fix with tape. Take cottons through C and fix with tape as far as heel. Pull cottons through slider, pull tight and fix with tape.

5 Glue BACK of SLIDER to strips of card.

strips of card

PUSHER

thicker than PUSHER

4 Glue strips of card to edges of slider. Lay PUSHER between strips. Pull frog forward and glue PUSHER to block on head.

2 Pieces of Springy Plastic from a pack of screws, etc. 7cm × 2½cm.

MATERIALS: Thin card: Yellow or white 9cm × 4cm: Black 15cm × 32cm:

Blue 15cm × 30cm. Stiff card: 15cm × 30cm. Glue.
2 Strips of card ½cm × 25cm. Cotton. Sticky tape.
2 Strips of thick card or thin wood 1cm × 30cm.

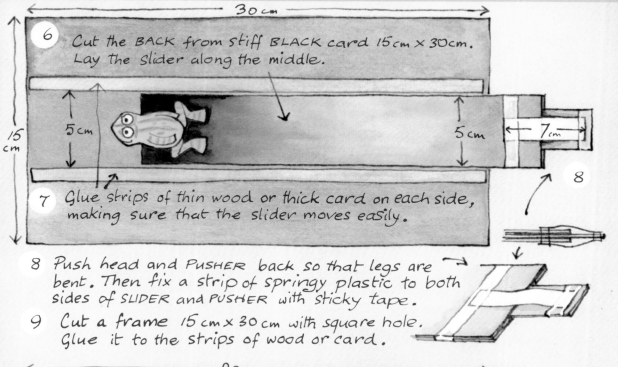

6 Cut the BACK from stiff BLACK card 15cm × 30cm.
   Lay the slider along the middle.

7 Glue strips of thin wood or thick card on each side,
   making sure that the slider moves easily.

8 Push head and PUSHER back so that legs are
   bent. Then fix a strip of springy plastic to both
   sides of SLIDER and PUSHER with sticky tape.

9 Cut a frame 15cm × 30cm with square hole.
   Glue it to the strips of wood or card.

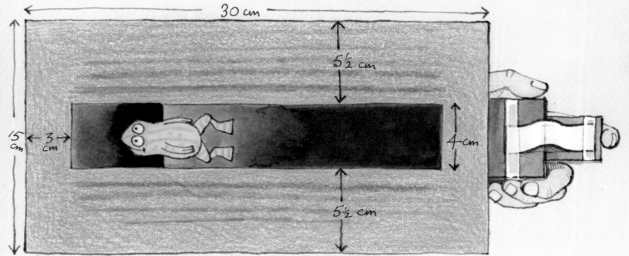

Two Snakes in the Water

a paper trick

TOOLS. Scissors, Craft-knife.

1 Cut this shape from paper or thin card. Cut wavy lines right across.

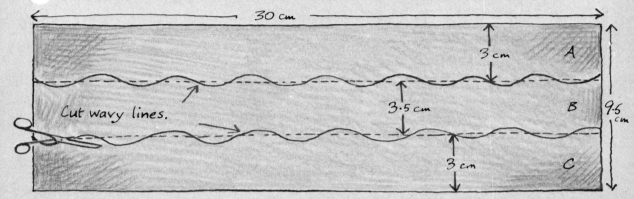

30 cm

3 cm   A

Cut wavy lines.   3·5 cm   B   9·5 cm

3 cm   C

2 Cut this shape from card. Glue strips of thick card as shown (very straight).

1 cm

BLACK   D

strips of card   3 cm   10 cm

1 cm   E

3 cm

1 cm   F

3 Cut 2 strips from thin card. Paint WHITE stripes on the ends.

SLIDER. Cut 2.

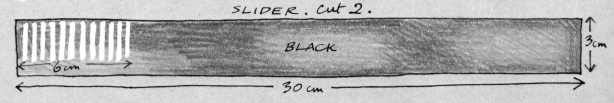

6 cm   BLACK   3 cm

30 cm

MATERIALS: a piece of thin blue card or thick paper 9·5cm × 30cm, a piece of black card 16cm × 30cm. White card 3cm × 7cm, 3 strips of thick card 30cm × 1cm, Glue, White & black paint.

SNAKE'S HEAD. Cut 2 pieces this size from thin white card.

Draw BLACK stripes to match stripes on sliders.

Glue heads at bottom of necks at G, 4cm from end of sliders.

⑤ Glue wavy piece A to strip D.

Fit slider, with head outside. Glue wavy piece B to strip E,

leaving 3mm gap between wavy edges. Put in second slider. Glue wavy piece C to strip F. Glue paper strips to cover ends.

Paint black wavy lines to match wavy gaps... Pull the SLIDER.

Punk Hippo the easiest puppet in the world....

you need: 4 buttons (2 with metal rings) 10 safety pins, elastic band:

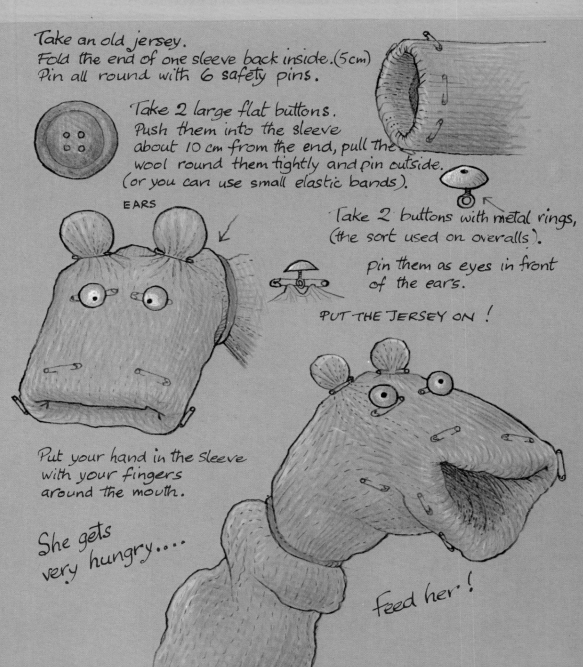

Take an old jersey.
Fold the end of one sleeve back inside.(5cm)
Pin all round with 6 safety pins.

Take 2 large flat buttons.
Push them into the sleeve
about 10 cm from the end, pull the
wool round them tightly and pin outside.
(or you can use small elastic bands).

EARS

Take 2 buttons with metal rings,
(the sort used on overalls).

pin them as eyes in front
of the ears.

PUT THE JERSEY ON !

Put your hand in the sleeve
with your fingers
around the mouth.

She gets
very hungry....

feed her !

.... and, on the other hand, **Simple People**

pieces of felt, fur, small safety pins, elastic band, scissors, needle, cotton.

You can make all sorts of puppets in the same way. Cut bits of fur into moustache or hair.

EYES

Cut shapes out of coloured felt to make eyes, noses, lips or even tongue.

LIPS

Sew safety pins on to the back of each piece. Two on long pieces, such as lips.

NOSE

Use same ears as Hippo, but at the side. Pin the lips at the end of the sleeve. Pin the other features where you like. The elastic band around the wrist helps to hold it tight on your fingers.

This one likes rock music... Play him a record and see if he can mime to it!

6. The Starling

It didn't take the Artist long to make his tea. He was in a bit of a hurry. He made a delicious cheese and lettuce sandwich with a sprinkling of chopped onions. He washed it down with a mug of tea and washed up.

It was a lovely warm evening. He wanted to sit in his garden by the river until the sun went down. In the evening if it was fine, he liked to listen to the plop of the fish and the songs of the birds.

This evening, his friends Emily and Ross were calling on their way home from school. Ross had promised to show the Artist a new paper trick he had learned.

'Hello,' called Ross. 'Sorry we're late.'

'Ah! there you are,' said the Artist.

'Lovely evening,' said Emily. 'I hope we haven't kept you waiting.'

'That's all right,' said the Artist. 'I don't mind waiting when there's a song to hear. Listen to that blackbird. Can you hear it over there in the woods?'

'I can hear it,' said Emily. 'But it's not in the woods. It's on that telegraph pole. I can see it.'

'Oh, that one,' said the Artist. 'That's no blackbird. It's the old starling up to his tricks again.'

'It does sound like a blackbird,' said Ross. 'And it looks like one too.'

'The starling is a mimic,' said the Artist. 'He'll copy anyone. Why, I even knew one who whistled the first line of "All Things Bright and Beautiful!"'

'However did he learn that?' asked Emily.

'The dairyman used to whistle it while he milked the cows in the morning. The starling got it from him. But you can always pick out a starling. He's covered with little stars. Come inside and I'll tell you how he got them.'

'We were hoping you would,' said Ross with a smile.

'In a cave there lived a wizard,' began the Artist. 'His name was Wizard Wagstaff.

Now some wizards are wicked. You know the type. They turn up in a puff of smoke and play nasty tricks on people. Turn them into toads or make hair grow on their noses or turn their babies into little piglets, that sort of thing.

This one was not like that. Oh, no. Wizard Wagstaff stayed in his cave making up new spells for his magic books. He only used them when he was asked.

The people of the village knew him well. They liked Wizard Wagstaff because his spells were all good spells. If their children had mumps or measles they would send for the wizard. He would be sure to have a spell to make them better.

Wizard Wagstaff had invented some very good spells. Spells for curing tummy-ache and warts; getting rid of nettles and carrot fly. In his big book of special spells he even had spells for making the chickens lay more eggs. One spell charmed the cows into giving more milk.

This was a very popular one because he did it with music. This is how he did it. He would take twelve singing birds to the dairy. The birds would sit on his "Special Portable Perch" and sing their sweetest song, in harmony, while the milkmaids milked the cows. Well, you know how, even today, they play the radio in the cowshed to keep the cows happy. It does seem to improve the milking.

But then the Wizard started to beat time with his magic wand and spoke the magic words . . .

He said:

"Oddle-me-doddle
serve us milk,
rich with cream
and smooth as silk.
Song of bird and swish of tail,
Abracadabra,
Fill the pail."

And the milk would flow! The milkmaids said it was the creamiest they had ever seen!

Well, one morning he was in the milking parlour doing his magic spell with a flock of blackbirds. He'd almost finished – they were on the last cow of all – and the farmer had given a saucer of milk to the farm cats.

The cats sniffed at the warm milk, turned up their pink noses, and walked away with their tails in the air.

"That's odd," said the farmer. "They've never done that before." He tasted a drop of the milk.

"Stop! stop!" he cried. "This milk is sour!"

"Impossible," said the Wizard. "The cats are not thirsty."

"It is, look," said the farmer.

"The Wizard looked into all the other buckets. He did not need to taste the milk. He could see that it had curdled. The milk was all lumpy and sour!

"Well, I'll be spellbound!" said Wizard Wagstaff. "That's never happened before. Perhaps the blackbirds don't like the cats in the dairy. We'll try again tonight . . . without the cats."

So that evening when milking time came, they tried again. They shut the cats in the kitchen.

The Wizard waved his wand.
The birds began to sing.
The Wizard said:
   "Oddle-me-doddle
   serve us milk,
   rich with cream
   and smooth as silk.
   Song of bird and swish of tail,
   Abracadabra,
   Fill the pail."
And the milk began to flow. As
each bucket was filled the farmer
tasted it. But the same thing had
happened! All the milk had turned
sour.

"It must be these birds," said the
Wizard. "They've been singing rather
too much lately. I'll get a new flock
tomorrow."

Tomorrow came. Wizard Wagstaff
arrived early with a cage of different
blackbirds.

"Everything should go well today," he said. "These are the finest
singing birds from the next valley. I
borrowed them from my cousin,
Wizard Wigglesworth."

He opened the cage. The birds flew
onto the Special Portable Perch.

Wizard Wagstaff waved his wand.
The birds began to sing.
The Wizard said:
   "Oddle-me-doddle
   serve us milk,
   rich with cream
   and smooth as silk.
   Song of bird and swish of tail,
   Abracadabra,
   Fill the pail."
And the milk began to flow. But
again, as each bucket filled it turned
sour.

"We'll finish without the spell,
thank you," said the farmer. He

71

waited for the worried Wizard to leave with his birds.

Wizard Wagstaff spoke sharply to the birds.

"What's the matter with you," he said. "You're not trying. Do you want me to tell Wizard Wigglesworth that you can't perform any more? You know what will happen. You'll be out on your tails in no time! It will be back to poking around for worms and pecking for rotten cherries. And as for me . . . I'll be redundant. There's no work for a worthless wizard these days!"

He was very angry. He wagged his finger at the blackbirds. Then he stopped looking angry. He looked surprised.

He counted the birds on the perch.

"One, two, three, four, five, six, seven, eight, nine, ten, eleven, twelve, . . . thirteen! That's it," cried Wizard Wagstaff. "Unlucky thirteen! There's one too many. And not only that. One of our birds is not a real blackbird. No wonder the milk went sour!"

He put his hand deep into his magic pocket. He took out a pepper-pot.

"We don't want to make that mistake again," he said. "I think this will do the trick."

Wizard Wagstaff waved his wand.

He called his blackbirds back into the cage leaving the other bird sitting alone on the perch. Then he sprinkled it all over with the magic pepper. At once it was covered with little stars.

"Now we'll be able to pick you out from all the other blackbirds," said the Wizard. "We will call you 'Starling', because of all the little silver stars."

And from that moment all the other starlings in the world sparkled with stars. Of course the starlings were very proud of their starry feathers. You can tell that by the proud way they walk with their chests stuck out.

But at least Wizard Wagstaff and Wizard Wigglesworth and all the other wizards in the world never had any more trouble with starlings, and the milk is always good. The other wizards were very grateful as they'd had the same trouble. So they made

Wizard Wagstaff their chief – they called him the *Star* wizard. He went around in a painted cart pulled by his donkey. Inside the cart he carried his cages of blackbirds, his black cat called Zoot and one little silver cage with a starling inside.

Because, sometimes, when he had finished his real work, Wizard Wagstaff would take the starling in its little silver cage into the farmhouse.

He would gather all the farmers' children together and entertain them with magic tricks.

He would do card tricks and disappearing tricks; tricks with bottles of coloured water and tricks with magic rings.

And then, at the end, he would bring out the starling who would do impersonations of all the other birds, and even make them laugh by copying the tunes their fathers whistled.'

The Artist finished his story. Out of the open window, by the light of the moon, he could still see the starling singing his heart out on the telegraph pole.

'Listen,' whispered Emily. 'He's trying to copy the nightingale now.'

'I know,' replied the Artist. 'He'll never learn. Now Ross, what was this trick you were going to show me?'

Ross showed the Artist his paper trick. It was how to make a paper star with only one cut of the scissors. What a coincidence!

Mimics of Song . . .

Many other birds are mimics. Parrots budgerigars and mynah birds are well-known as pets.

The male Lyre bird performs his song and dance on one of several mounds of earth in its territory. His song includes imitations of other birds and animals; even the sounds of motorhorns and the whine of circular saws.

THE LYRE BIRD
(Australia)

He starts the song on a branch then hops down to perform his dance. He swings his tail forward to make a shimmering canopy, singing while he finishes the dance.

THE WHYDAH.
an African "cuckoo"

The African Whydar lays her egg in the nest of a weaver-finch.

The male mimics the call of his foster-mother.

The female is attracted to the male by the call she recognises. This makes sure that the chick that hatches in the nest of the chosen finch, makes the correct begging calls.

. . . Colour and Shape

Some creatures mimic their surroundings.

<u>KALLIMA inachus</u> (S.E.Asia)
These are known as
'DEAD LEAF' butterflies.
Although their bright colours
show up when flying, when
they settle in a tree and close
their wings, they look exactly
like a dead leaf.

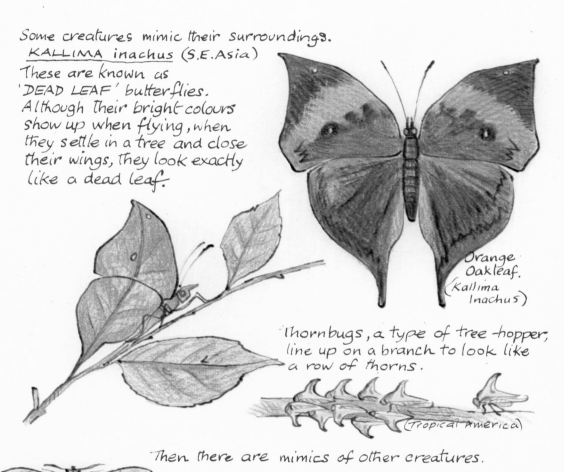

Orange
Oakleaf.
(Kallima
Inachus)

Thornbugs, a type of tree-hopper,
line up on a branch to look like
a row of thorns.

(Tropical America)

Then there are mimics of other creatures.

The <u>HORNET CLEARWING MOTH</u>
and the <u>HOVERFLY</u> both look
very much like the
more dangerous
wasps and
Hornets.

<u>COMMON
WASP</u>

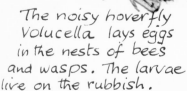

The noisy hoverfly
Volucella lays eggs
in the nests of bees
and wasps. The larvae
live on the rubbish.

A Paper Star *in just one cut.*

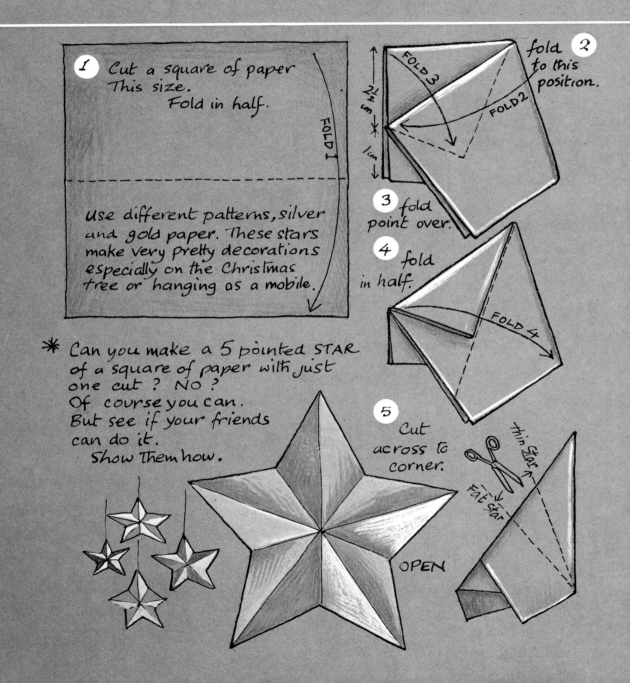

1 Cut a square of paper This size.
        Fold in half.

Use different patterns, silver and gold paper. These stars make very pretty decorations especially on the Christmas tree or hanging as a mobile.

FOLD 1

2 fold to this position.

FOLD 3   FOLD 2

$2\frac{1}{2}$ 3" 1cm

3 fold point over.

4 fold in half.

FOLD 4

* Can you make a 5 pointed STAR of a square of paper with just one cut? NO?
Of course you can.
But see if your friends can do it.
    Show Them how.

5 Cut across to corner.

thin Star
Fat Star

OPEN

Singing Birds — *tweeting* a greeting card

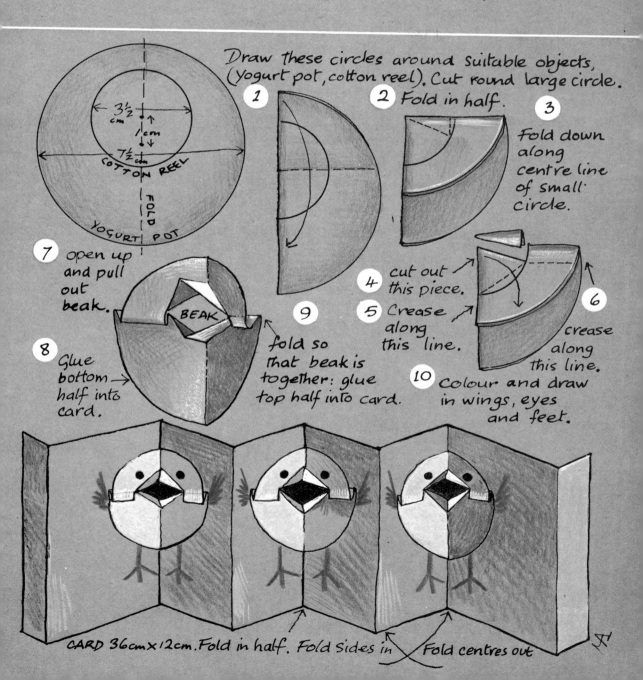

Draw these circles around suitable objects, (yogurt pot, cotton reel). Cut round large circle.

3½ cm
1 cm
7½ cm
COTTON REEL
FOLD
YOGURT POT

1

2 Fold in half.

3 Fold down along centre line of small circle.

4 cut out this piece.

5 Crease along this line.

6 crease along this line.

7 open up and pull out beak.

8 Glue bottom half into card.

9 fold so that beak is together: glue top half into card.

BEAK

10 Colour and draw in wings, eyes and feet.

CARD 36cm × 12cm. Fold in half. Fold sides in — Fold centres out

A Birds' Nest finger puppets

TOOLS: scissors . needle.

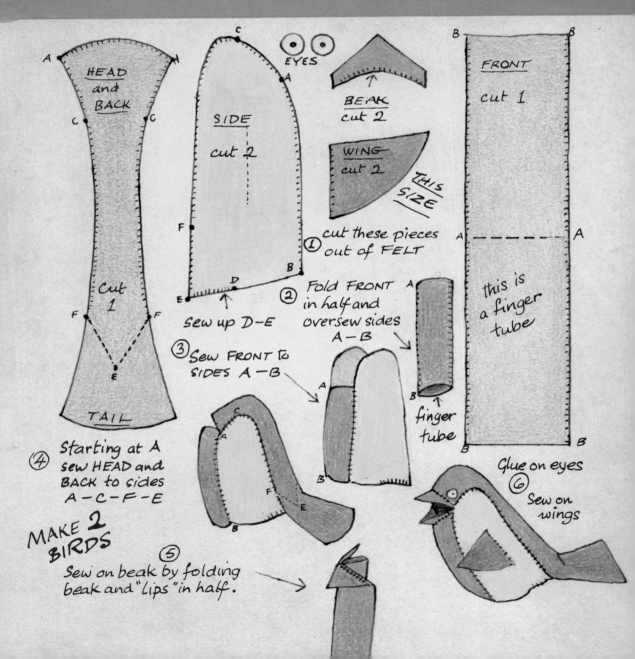

HEAD and BACK

Cut 1

TAIL

SIDE

cut 2

Sew up D-E

EYES

BEAK
cut 2

WING
cut 2

THIS SIZE

① cut these pieces out of FELT

② Fold FRONT in half and oversew sides A—B

③ Sew FRONT to SIDES A—B

finger tube

FRONT

cut 1

this is a finger tube

④ Starting at A sew HEAD and BACK to sides A-C-F-E

MAKE 2 BIRDS

⑤ Sew on beak by folding beak and "lips" in half.

Glue on eyes

⑥ Sew on wings

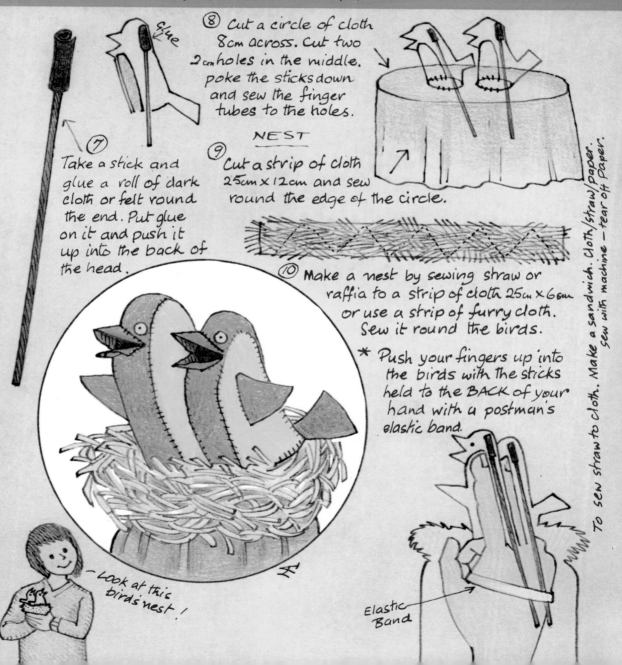

Glue

⑧ Cut a circle of cloth 8 cm across. Cut two 2 cm holes in the middle. Poke the sticks down and sew the finger tubes to the holes.

⑦ Take a stick and glue a roll of dark cloth or felt round the end. Put glue on it and push it up into the back of the head.

NEST

⑨ Cut a strip of cloth 25 cm × 12 cm and sew round the edge of the circle.

⑩ Make a nest by sewing straw or raffia to a strip of cloth 25 cm × 6 cm or use a strip of furry cloth. Sew it round the birds.

* Push your fingers up into the birds with the sticks held to the BACK of your hand with a postman's elastic band.

- Look at this bird's nest!

Elastic Band

To sew straw to cloth. Make a sandwich. Cloth/straw/paper. Sew with machine – tear off paper.

7. Jack's Flowers

At the bottom of John's garden was a jetty sticking out into the river. That was where John tied up his rowing boat. But today there was no boat there, because John had gone visiting.

He had spent several days making Christmas cards to send to all his friends. He had painted some, he had made some very funny ones by pasting bits of magazine pictures together and he had stuck dried leaves and flowers onto coloured card.

Today he was taking a card to his friend, the Artist, who lived across the river. John found it much quicker to go there by boat than to walk round by the bridge in the town.

So there is John's boat, tied up to a ring at the bottom of the steps that lead up to the Artist's garden. And there is John in the Artist's studio.

'I've brought you a card,' he said.

'How kind,' said the Artist as he took it out of the envelope. 'I like that. Dried flowers and leaves. Very pretty.'

I thought you'd rather have that than a painted one,' said John. 'After all, you seem to have a lot of painted cards.'

'Yes, most of my old friends send me hand-made cards,' said the Artist, 'and they're mostly painted ones. Yours is a nice change.'

'Shall I help you put the cards on the shelf?' asked John.

'That's very kind of you,' said the Artist. 'But the shelf is a bit dusty. Are you any good at dusting?'

'Oh yes, I often help with the dusting at home.'

'Good,' said the Artist. 'I will take down my precious china ornaments and put them on the table. I wouldn't like them to get broken.'

So the Artist took down all his precious china ornaments and stood them carefully on the table.

There was a fisherman and his wife, two cottages, a castle, a sea captain, a pair of cats covered in flowers, a sailor in a straw hat and a funny-looking zebra that was more like a horse with stripes.

'What funny old ornaments!' said John as he dusted the shelf. 'Flowery cats and stripey horses! Why *are* the cats all covered in flowers?'

'Well, I suppose somebody painted them,' said the Artist.

'Who?' insisted John. 'And who painted stripes on the horse and turned it into a zebra?'

'Well, if you've finished the dusting you deserve a rest. Sit in the big armchair. I'll tell you the story while I finish this card which I'm painting for a very good friend of mine.'

'It's really the sailor's story,' he began. His name was Jack and before he went to sea he lived with his parents in a white-washed seaside cottage.

Jack's father was a fisherman and his mother sold fish in the market.

But Jack was no good at fishing or selling fish. In fact, there was only one thing he was any good at, and that was painting flowers.

He painted flower pictures; he painted flowers on the walls of his bedroom; when he was quite tiny he even painted flowers all over his toy soldiers!

82

His mother thought it was rather lovely, but his father said he was wasting his time.

"Give him something useful to do!" he ordered.

So Jack's mum put him to painting the price-tickets for her boxes of fish. It was just painting numbers but you can guess what happened. The tickets ended up covered in flowers so that you could hardly read the price!

Some people tried to pay for the fish with flowers instead of money. They were all very amused.

But Jack's dad was annoyed!

'If he likes painting so much, let him paint the cottage – WHITE!" he said.

So Jack was left with a large pot of white paint while mum and dad went off to work. He painted the cottage very nicely, but as he had some paint left, he wondered what would happen if he mixed other things with it.

Blackcurrant juice made it pink and a little mud made it grey. Squashed walnut shells made a strong brown and writing ink made a blue. Soon, what with curry powder and blue-bag, he soon had enough colours to be at his flowery tricks again!

When mum and dad got home he had got as far as the chimney stacks as the walls were a mass of painted flowers. The neighbours thought it was very funny. They came to point and laugh.

"Very original, I'm sure," said the postman, as he searched among the flowers for the letterbox, "but rather confusing."

"This won't do at all," grumbled Jack's dad. "We're plain ordinary folk, and now everyone comes to stare at us. That boy has made us a laughing stock!"

"Perhaps he'll grow out of it," said Jack's mum, hopefully.

"Grow out of it!" thundered Jack's dad. "He's already twenty-three! What that lad needs is a man's job. We'll send him to sea."

Luckily, a sea-captain was in port looking for a crew. All the likely lads who wanted to see the world had signed on. He had found seamen and sailmakers, carpenters and cooks. As the ship had a big steam engine to drive the paddle-wheels when there was no wind, he also had engineers, stokers and greasers.

But it was a large ship and the captain still needed more men. So Jack's parents dressed. him in bell-bottomed trousers, a blue jacket and a straw hat to keep off the sun – just like a real sailor – and took him down to the harbour.

The ship was tied up alongside the town quay with all the other barges, barques and brigantines. It was easy to find because beside the gangplank, that's the plank you walk up to get on board, there was a notice. "Hands wanted. See the World. Good pay. Good Food. Sign on Here."

Jack and his parents walked up the gangplank, admiring the sailors getting the ship ready for sea. Some were coiling ropes, some were scrubbing the deck. The young ones were learning how to tie knots and put up the sails. They were polishing the brass and loading coal for the boiler.

"Now this is man's work," said Jack's dad. "A year or two of this life will do Jack the world of good. Make him a man. Knock all that flower-painting nonsense out of his head."

"I do hope the Captain will take him on," said Jack's mum.

The Captain was leaning out of the cabin window watering his window box. He was smartly dressed and wore a flower-embroidered waistcoat. He fixed his fierce beady eye on Jack.

"So you want to join my ship? You'll have to make yourself useful. Can you tie knots? Or reef a sail? Or box the compass?"

"I'm willing to learn," said Jack. "But I'm very good with a paintbrush."

"Ah, a painter," said the Captain. "The ship could do with a coat of paint. Would you like to sign on as ship's painter?"

Jack looked at the Captain's waistcoat.

"I'll give it a try," he said.

So Jack went to sea as ship's painter. The ship steamed out of port, a sturdy ship, built of oak and teak. But the paintwork was flaking and the varnish was peeling. Jack soon altered that.

As the sails were hoisted and a brisk easterly breeze filled them Jack was already at work. He scraped the loose paint off as they lost sight of land, and by the time they had sighted the rocks of Brittany he had prepared the ship for painting.

As they crossed the Bay of Biscay he could be seen halfway up the mast, varnishing the spars, and by the time they reached the coast of Spain, he had painted the paddle-wheel covers and the cabins.

When they tied up in the quiet port of Santander he managed to get the figurehead painted. Then he got down to the details.

He found plenty of coloured paints on board. The figurehead needed decorating. Soon she was covered in flowers. Then he decorated the cabin doors and the rails. He did a specially good job with the flowers on the paddle-wheel covers and even the funnel could be painted now the fires were out.

It was a very different ship from the one that had steamed away from the white cliffs of Dover.

"You know, lad," said the Captain. "What with your painting and my window-boxes, the old tub is a sight for sore eyes. Look, even the sail-makers have taken up embroidery and decorated the sails. I always did fancy a few flowers about the place. In fact, to tell you the truth, I never really liked the sea. I always wanted to keep a market garden and grow flowers.''

So, as Jack had used up all the ship's paint anyway, and they were eager to show the people back home their handsome ship, they decided to set sail for home. Jack had missed his mum and dad and the Captain thought he might get enough money if he sold his smart ship to buy a small piece of land he had his eye on in Kent.

Meanwhile, at home, things had changed. The pretty cottage had become famous. People came from all over the land to see it.

Jack's mum served teas (with fresh fish) to the visitors, and Jack's dad ran trips across the bay in his fishing boat. They had sold every one of Jack's flower paintings and made a lot of money.

So when someone came rushing up from the harbour one day shouting: ''A sail! A sail! A flowery sail,'' they were overjoyed. They welcomed Jack home with open arms and tears of happiness.

"Oh, Jack my boy,'' said his dad. ''I was wrong to send you away. You belong here, at home with mother and me. If it's flowers you want to paint, you paint flowers. Here, I've bought paints. You can start at once on that wall.''

So Jack went on painting flowers. He painted all the other cottages. He painted plates and cups to sell in the shop. He was even asked to paint the castle on the cliff (He didn't notice the two white cats asleep in the sun, so I'm afraid they got painted too.) The place became even more famous and Jack was the most famous person in the whole village.'

'There,' said the Artist. 'So that's the story of the sailor and the flowery cats. Shall we put up the cards now?'

'But what about the zebra?' asked John. 'Surely he didn't paint that too?'

'Oh, yes,' replied the Artist, 'so many people came up to him while he was working and said, as people will:

"Oh, you are clever, painting all those flowers, why, I couldn't even draw a straight line!" that he thought he would try that for a change. You know, try to paint straight lines instead of flowers. But he only did it once, on the white horse and thought the result so dull that he never painted anything but flowers ever again.

He just went on happily painting flowers. Look at this card I've just painted for your Christmas Card. It's all there: the cottages, the ship in the bay, the castle and all the rest; and see, there's Jack painting flowers, he just went on and on and on and on ... Oh yes, on and on and on and on ...'

Swinging Sailor

MATERIALS: thin card, thread, wood or cane, glue.

TOOLS: Scissors, Drill, crayons or felt pens.

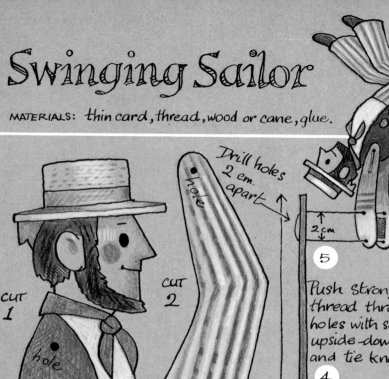

CUT 1

hole

CUT 2

hole

Drill holes 2 cm. apart

5 Push strong thread through holes with sailor upside-down and tie knot.

2 cm

40 cm

4 Use springy wood cane or bamboo about 1 cm square.

CUT 2

hole

holes

If you fix the poles to the bar with thin nails or pins, it is best to drill the holes first. Fix with glue or sticky tape for strength.

1 Cut these pieces out of thin card.

2 Make holes.

fix arms and legs with a short piece of cotton glued to the outside.

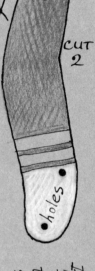

fix with glue or tape.

3 Glue a piece of wood or cork 1 cm thick between hands clear of holes.

10 cm

this can be any piece of strong wood.

16 cm

6 Gently squeeze the bottom of the poles and see him jump.

Jack-in-a-Box a flowery sea-chest

TOOLS: scissors, 3cm wide tube.

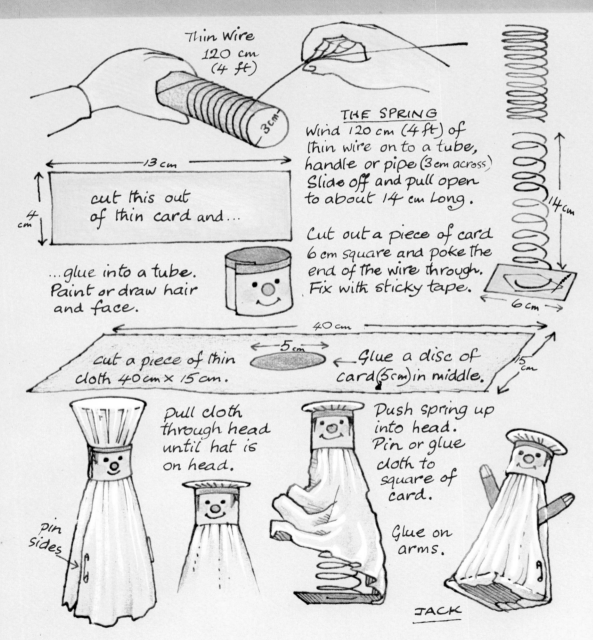

Thin Wire 120 cm (4 ft)

3cm

THE SPRING

Wind 120 cm (4 ft) of thin wire on to a tube, handle or pipe (3cm across). Slide off and pull open to about 14 cm long.

Cut out a piece of card 6 cm square and poke the end of the wire through. Fix with sticky tape.

6 cm

14 cm

13 cm

4 cm

cut this out of thin card and...

...glue into a tube. Paint or draw hair and face.

40 cm

5 cm

15 cm

cut a piece of thin cloth 40cm × 15cm.

Glue a disc of card (5cm) in middle.

Pull cloth through head until hat is on head.

Push spring up into head. Pin or glue cloth to square of card.

Glue on arms.

pin sides

JACK

MATERIALS: thin card 26 cm x 26 cm. thin cloth 40 cm x 15 cm. thin iron wire 120cm long. Glue, matchstick, paint, felt pens or crayons.

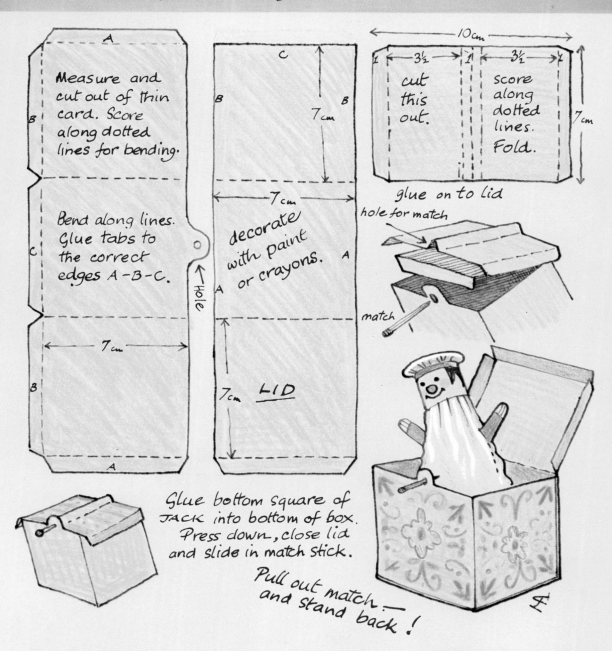

A

B

Measure and cut out of thin card. Score along dotted lines for bending.

Bend along lines. Glue tabs to the correct edges A-B-C.

7cm

B

A

C

B

B

7cm

← Hole

7cm

decorate with paint or crayons.

A

A

7cm LID

A

10cm

½ 3½ 1 3½ ½

cut this out.

score along dotted lines. Fold.

7cm

glue on to lid

hole for match

match

Glue bottom square of JACK into bottom of box. Press down, close lid and slide in match stick.

Pull out match — and stand back!

Paddle-steamer *a moving picture*

TOOLS : craft knife , scissors, sharp point.

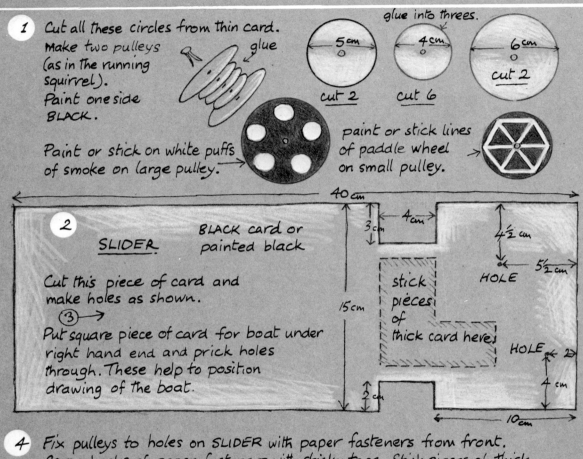

1 Cut all these circles from thin card.
Make two pulleys
(as in the running
squirrel).
Paint one side
BLACK.

glue

glue into threes.

5 cm — cut 2

4 cm — cut 6

6 cm — cut 2

Paint or stick on white puffs
of smoke on large pulley.

paint or stick lines
of paddle wheel
on small pulley.

2 SLIDER   BLACK card or painted black

Cut this piece of card and
make holes as shown.

③ →

Put square piece of card for boat under
right hand end and prick holes
through. These help to position
drawing of the boat.

stick
pieces
of
thick card here

40 cm

3 cm

4 cm

4½ cm

5½ cm

HOLE

15 cm

HOLE ← 2

4 cm

2 cm

10 cm

4 Fix pulleys to holes on SLIDER with paper fasteners from front.
Cover backs of paper fasteners with sticky tape. Stick pieces of thick
card to SLIDER. Cut thick card 40 cm X 20 cm. for back of picture.

5 Stick strips of
wood to thick
card each side
of SLIDER.

move slider left and pull thick
thread into notches. Wind once
round pulleys to other notches

cut notches for thread.

cut notches.   fix thread at back with sticky tape.

MATERIALS: 3 pieces of thin card 40cm × 25cm, one black if possible.
1 piece thick card 40cm × 25cm. Thread or thin string.
2 paper fasteners, Black paint. Crayons. Glue.
2 strips of soft wood ½cm × 1 cm, 40 cm long (or thick card).

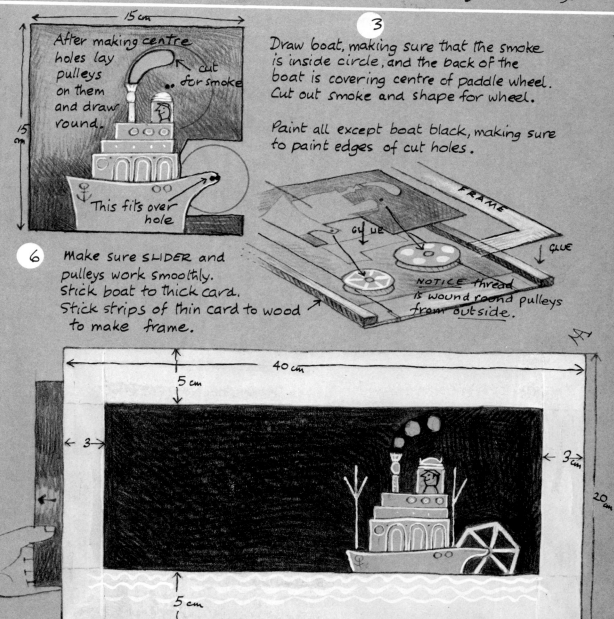

15 cm

After making centre holes lay pulleys on them and draw round.

cut for smoke

15 cm

This fits over hole

3

Draw boat, making sure that the smoke is inside circle, and the back of the boat is covering centre of paddle wheel. Cut out smoke and shape for wheel.

Paint all except boat black, making sure to paint edges of cut holes.

FRAME

GLUE

GLUE

NOTICE thread is wound round pulleys from outside.

6 Make sure SLIDER and pulleys work smoothly. Stick boat to thick card. Stick strips of thin card to wood to make frame.

40 cm

5 cm

3

3 cm

20 cm

5 cm

8. Moving Mole

Linda was sitting in the Artist's big armchair reading a book. The Artist was standing by the window looking very angry.

'Look at that!' he said. 'He's taken a short cut – right across the lawn!'

Linda looked up from her book.

'What's doing what?'

'All those heaps of dirt,' said the Artist. 'A mole has made his tunnel under the lawn. I didn't know we had moles.'

'Perhaps he's a stranger and doesn't know his way about yet,' said Linda. 'Perhaps he's only just moved in.'

'It's very annoying,' said the Artist. 'Just when I've got the grass looking tidy.'

'You'll have to put up notices,' said Linda. 'NO DIGGING, MOLES KEEP OUT, something like that. Though I don't suppose moles can read.'

'Parky could,' said the Artist. 'He could write too. He sent a letter.'

'Who's Parky?' asked Linda.

'Parky was a mole,' said the Artist, thoughtfully. 'He moved out into the country. He used to live in a London park. That's how he got his name. But he had to move. Shall I tell you about it?'

Linda settled down deep into the big armchair.

'I'd like that,' she said.

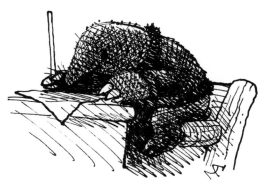

'You could tell he wasn't a country mole,' said the Artist. 'You could tell that by the way he talked.'

Linda looked up, puzzled.

'Oh yes,' went on the Artist. 'A real cockney, born within the sound of Bow bells and all that sort of thing.

You see there are plenty of parks in London where the ground is soft enough for digging.

Parky lived in one of these parks. He had quite a good life. There were flowers in the spring. There were shady bushes and trees whose fallen leaves kept the ground soft and damp. It was just right for Parky to dig for the worms and grubs that he liked to eat. His house was under the pavement at the end of a tunnel.

Most of the day he stayed in his underground home. At night, when he was out hunting for his supper, he would go quite close to the railings and the pavement that surrounded the park.

He noticed that the cars in the street had different sorts of number plates and letters. There was 'B' for Belgium, 'P' for Poland, 'F' for France and even 'E' for Spain because Sweden had already got 'S'. Seeing these cars from all over the world made Parky think that he would like to travel to other countries, but of course he couldn't – he had no money. He couldn't even leave the park.

The road ran right round the park and the cars and taxis whizzing round day and night made it far too dangerous to cross. Then, under the road there were gas-pipes and cables. The great brick sewer ran there too, and the water-pipes, so there was no way to tunnel out of the park.

So, you ask, how did Parky get there in the first place?

Well, he wasn't the only mole in the park. His brothers and sisters and cousins lived there too. Moles had lived in that place for hundreds of years. His mum and dad; his grandads and his grandmas; and all the great- and great-great- and great-great-great-grandparents had lived there.

I dare say they'd lived there before there were roads or cars or even a city there. They'd probably been there when it was just part of a big field leading down to the river Thames.

Anyhow, Parky called it home and there he was stuck. Until the parking meters came!

One day he was woken up by the noise of road-drills. He crept out to the railings to see what was going on.

On the pavement over his house the road workers had put up a sort of tent where they were making tea. Along the path he could see a great machine throbbing and rumbling.

From it came tubes and wires leading to a road drill. A very hairy man was holding on to the rattling road drill and breaking up the path over Parky's house!

The noise was terrible! And the dust! It was all over his furniture and his bed was full of bits of stone and dirt.

It didn't last long. They were very quick workers and soon moved on to the next bit of path. As soon as the drilling stopped, Parky tidied up. He swept and dusted. He shook the dirt out of his sheets and washed them. Luckily the hole in his ceiling was like a chimney and the draught took the dust up like smoke.

Then Parky heard a lorry unloading something onto the pavement.

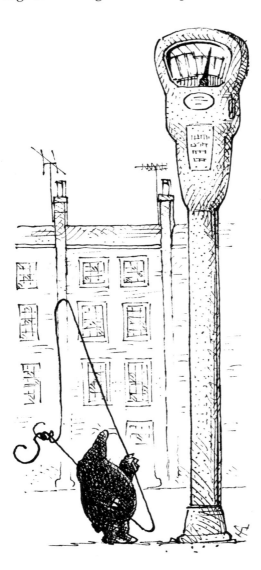

When he went to look he saw that they were poking poles into the pavement. On top of these poles there were things like clocks.

Parky looked at the writing on the side of the lorry. It said: 'London Parking Meters Limited'. Parky did not know what 'Parking Meters' meant. He found out later, but at first he thought the poles were some kind of chimney, because the end of one stuck right down into his bedroom!

It had pushed more stones and dirt into his room and he'd only just tidied it. He tried to sweep up but now the dust had nowhere to go. It just flew up in great clouds and settled again.

"This chimney isn't very good," he thought. "It must be blocked."

So he searched around in the park until he found a piece of stiff wire.

"This will soon clear the chimney," he said. He poked the wire up the pipe as far as he could. Of course, he didn't realise that the meter on top stopped the wire going right through, but his wire did break the plastic money box inside.

So his room stayed just as dusty as ever and bits of broken plastic fell onto his bed.

"It's no good," he moaned. "I shall have to move."

Now Parky had a friend who lived in the country. Parky's friend was a coypu – that's a sort of large water rat with a thick tail and big orange front teeth.

Coypus live by the river. They make holes in the river-bank and eat reeds and roots and all sorts of vegetables. They really love their greens!

Parky knew that his friend Muskit (that was the Coypu's name) was just the person to know about country property – houses and places to live – along the river. There were all sorts of holes and burrows in the river bank. There were homes for rats, voles, kingfishers and other animals and birds. Muskit knew them all.

So Parky decided to write a letter to Muskit. He sent it by pigeon post. He wrote:

Dear Muskit,

I hope you are well. I am suffering from a very bad attack of parking meters. I cannot live here any longer. I must find a new home. If there is an empty burrow or the space for digging one, I should be glad to hear of it.

Love, Parky.

Muskit answered by return of pigeon:

Dear Parky,

Plenty of room, come when you can. See you soon.

Love, Muskit.

This was easier said than done.

Parky had no money to move house, but it was the parking meters that solved his problem in the end.

You know that if anyone wants to park they have to put in a five- or ten-penny piece. But up to now this had not happened. The meters were not used until a whole row had been installed. Plastic bags, with 'Not in use' printed on them, covered each meter.

Then the morning came when the work was all finished. All the plastic bags were taken off and from that moment on everyone had to pay to park. The money came rolling in, literally!

Parky was lying in his bed sipping his early morning tea when a five-penny piece came rattling down the tube and fell on his pillow. Then another rolled down and another. Soon they were all over his bed.

"My goodness! Pennies from heaven," gasped Parky. "Where's it all coming from?"

He pushed it off onto the floor. Later that day more money tumbled in. By the end of the week he was living in a tiny corner with hardly room to move! The rest of his house was full of money.

When the meter maid came to collect the money from all the meters, she found that one empty.

She telephoned the parking meter company and reported the fault.

"There's a broken meter," she said. "The money has all fallen through a hole. I'm afraid you'll have to dig it up again."

So the road drills came back. The noise and dust were terrible.

Parky made up his mind.

Pulling his suitcases out from under the huge pile of money, he filled them and all his pockets with the silver coins.

He only just managed to get out of his back door as the drill came through the ceiling.

He dragged the bags of money across the pavement to the taxi rank.

He hailed a taxi: "To Muskit's cottage, quickly," he said.

The taxi man was very helpful, lifting the bags into the taxi and finding out where to go, from the address on the letter.

So that's how Parky moved to the country.'

'I hope the journey didn't take too long,' said Linda.

'Why's that?'

'Well, it says here, in my animal book,' said Linda, 'that "a mole cannot live for more than a few hours without feeding."'

'Ah, well,' said the Artist. 'He probably had a few sandwiches with him, for the journey.'

'It also says "the mole's main food is worms; earthworms, cutworms and wireworms,"' went on Linda.

'I suppose there's nothing a mole likes better,' said the Artist, 'than a few tasty worm sandwiches.'

'When he got to the river,' said Linda, quickly changing the subject, 'he must have found it a lot quieter than the London park . . . but the money! Wasn't it stealing?'

'They did take his house without asking,' said the Artist. 'The money he took was a very small price to pay for that. London houses aren't cheap, you know!'

Parky's meter

a money box.

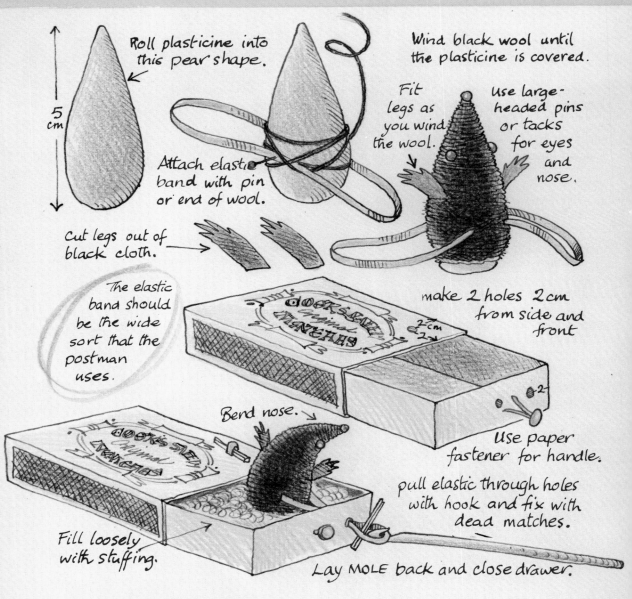

5 cm

Roll plasticine into this pear shape.

Attach elastic band with pin or end of wool.

Cut legs out of black cloth.

The elastic band should be the wide sort that the postman uses.

Wind black wool until the plasticine is covered.

Fit legs as you wind the wool.

Use large-headed pins or tacks for eyes and nose.

make 2 holes 2cm from side and front

2 cm

2

2

Bend nose.

Use paper fastener for handle.

pull elastic through holes with hook and fix with dead matches.

Fill loosely with stuffing.

Lay MOLE back and close drawer.

MATERIALS: Large Kitchen Matchbox (8 to 12 cm) Toilet roll tube. Plasticine. Small box to fit over tube (12 oxo box). Gum strip. Paste and paper. Black cloth. Black wool. Elastic band (7cm). Stuffing or Cotton wool. Pins. Paper fastener.

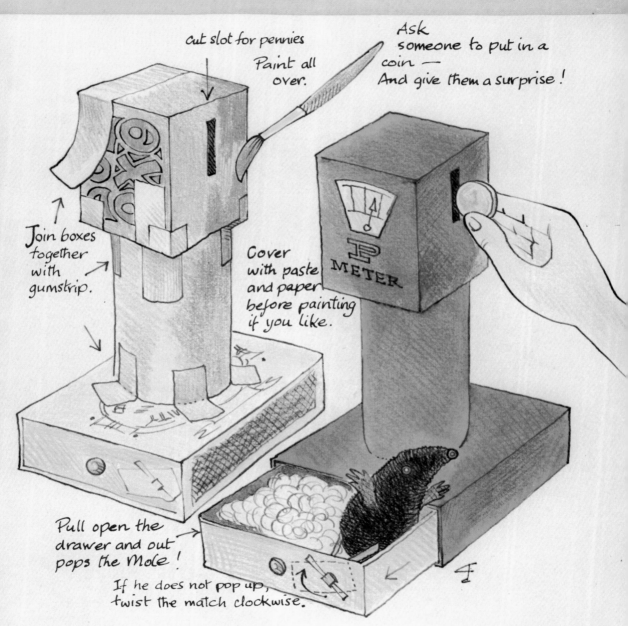

cut slot for pennies

Paint all over.

Ask someone to put in a coin — And give them a surprise!

Join boxes together with gumstrip.

Cover with paste and paper before painting if you like.

Pull open the drawer and out pops the Mole!

If he does not pop up, twist the match clockwise.

moving mole

TOOLS: Scissors. Paste brush. Nail file. Bowl or old cup 7cm wide. crochet hook or wire hook.

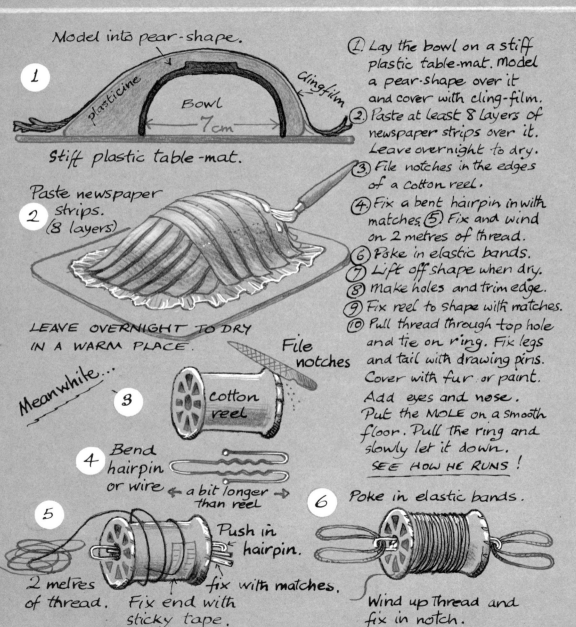

Model into pear-shape.

1 plasticine Bowl 7cm Clingfilm

Stiff plastic table-mat.

2 Paste newspaper strips. (8 layers)

LEAVE OVERNIGHT TO DRY IN A WARM PLACE.

Meanwhile...

3 cotton reel File notches

4 Bend hairpin or wire ← a bit longer than reel →

5 2 metres of thread. Push in hairpin. Fix end with sticky tape. fix with matches.

6 Poke in elastic bands. Wind up thread and fix in notch.

① Lay the bowl on a stiff plastic table-mat. Model a pear-shape over it and cover with cling-film.
② Paste at least 8 layers of newspaper strips over it. Leave overnight to dry.
③ File notches in the edges of a cotton reel.
④ Fix a bent hairpin in with matches. ⑤ Fix and wind on 2 metres of thread.
⑥ Poke in elastic bands.
⑦ Lift off shape when dry.
⑧ Make holes and trim edge.
⑨ Fix reel to shape with matches.
⑩ Pull thread through top hole and tie on ring. Fix legs and tail with drawing pins. Cover with fur or paint. Add eyes and nose. Put the MOLE on a smooth floor. Pull the ring and slowly let it down.
SEE HOW HE RUNS!

MATERIALS: Empty cotton reel. Hairpin or wire. 8 drawing pins. 2 elastic bands (7cm). Newspaper and paste. Matches. 2 metres of thread. Plasticine. Clingfilm. Curtain ring.

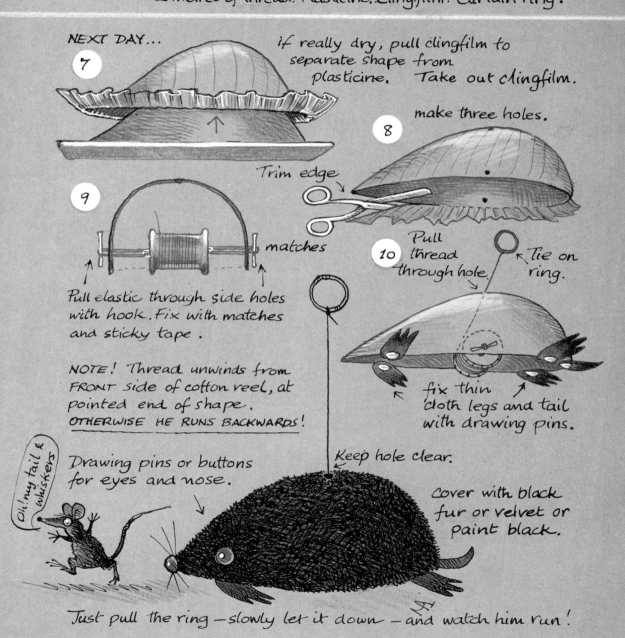

NEXT DAY...

7 if really dry, pull clingfilm to separate shape from plasticine. Take out clingfilm.

Trim edge

8 make three holes.

9 matches

Pull elastic through side holes with hook. Fix with matches and sticky tape.

NOTE! Thread unwinds from FRONT side of cotton reel, at pointed end of shape. OTHERWISE HE RUNS BACKWARDS!

10 Pull thread through hole. Tie on ring.

fix thin cloth legs and tail with drawing pins.

Keep hole clear.

Drawing pins or buttons for eyes and nose.

Oh! my tail & whiskers

Cover with black fur or velvet or paint black.

Just pull the ring — slowly let it down — and watch him run!

9. The Troll

The Artist was sitting on the river bank sketching a mass of flag irises on the other side.

It was a very hot day – not a cloud in sight – so he had found a shady place under the willow trees, out of the sun.

He wasn't the only one out on this hot afternoon. Craig was taking his little sister Lorna for a walk. They were hot and tired and Lorna didn't look at all happy.

'I'm thirsty,' she wailed.

'There's nothing to drink here,' said Craig.

'Waah!' she cried, pointing to the river.

'You can't drink that,' said Craig. 'That's river water. It's full of bugs and creepies!'

'I want a drink,' she persisted.

'You'll just have to wait 'til you get home,' said Craig. Then he noticed the man painting.

'Come on,' he said, trying to take her mind off drinking, 'let's go and see the man's picture.'

They walked over to the trees and studied the painting.

'Cor!' said Craig. 'I wish I could paint like that. Those yellow flowers look so real you can almost smell them.'

Lorna sniffed.

'Oh, it's not so hard,' said the Artist. 'You only have to draw what you see.'

Lorna sniffed again. The Artist turned round.

'Cheer up,' he said.

'I'm thirsty,' said Lorna. 'I want a drink.'

'Take no notice,' said Craig. 'She's always moaning.'

The Artist took a bottle out of his bag.

'It's for my painting really,' he said, 'but it's clean water from the tap. There's a little left.'

Lorna put out her hands to take the bottle.

'Oh no, you mustn't drink out of the bottle,' said the Artist. 'You need a cup.'

'Have you brought one?' asked Craig.

'No, but it won't take a minute to make one.'

The Artist tore a clean page from his sketch-book, folded it in half, then with a fold here and a tuck there produced a paper cup. He poured the water from the bottle and gave it to Lorna, who gulped it all down.

'Careful,' he said. Don't spill it down your dress.'

Lorna looked into the cup. She turned it over and shook it.

'It's all gone,' she said.

'Of course it's all gone,' said Craig. 'You've just swigged it all!'

'That's the trouble with Origami cups,' said the Artist – 'when you drink all the water, the cup is empty. It's not like that with Troll-cups.'

'Troll-cups?' repeated Lorna.

'Yes, it must be the magic sealing wax they use,' said the Artist. 'You can't empty a Troll-cup. It just goes on filling itself up. Look I'll tell you what, if you're still thirsty, come along to my studio. I'm packing up now because the midges are beginning to bite. You can have a drink and I'll tell you all about the Troll.'

'And will you show me how to make that paper cup?' asked Craig.

'The Origami cup?' said the Artist as he gathered up his things. 'Yes, if you like, I'll show you that too.'

In the studio the Artist gave them orange squash in real china cups.

'Now drink it slowly,' he said. 'You'll get a tummy-ache if you gulp it. Sit in the big armchair and sip it while I tell you about the Troll.'

"Once upon a time," began the Artist, "long, long ago in Denmark, a wooden church stood in a village in a green valley. It had real glass in the windows, a brass weather-cock and a tall steeple.

The people of the village were very proud of their fine church.

"See how the church pierces the sky with its slender steeple. It must be the tallest church in all of Jutland," said the people of the village.

But some of them were not satisfied with their church.

"It would be so much better with a bell," they said.

"A bell would ring out across the valley."

"It would remind people to come to church."

So all the people saved up their money. No one in the village was rich, but in time they had enough.

The new bell was fitted high up in the steeple.

Nearby in a wooden hut at the edge of the forest, lived a Troll. Like all trolls he was rather bad-tempered and like all trolls he just could not bear the sound of church bells!

So when the new bell began to ring he was very cross. The bell rang first thing in the morning and last thing at

night. The Troll built a strong door but the noise came in through the cracks. He put straw in the cracks but the sound of the bell came down the chimney, bounced across the floor and clanged in his ears!

He even tried sleeping under his mattress but it was no use. In the end he had to move. He packed his bags and went to live miles away in another forest where he could no longer hear the bell.

But he could not forget the comfortable hut where he had lived. His new home was a damp and murky cave. He became so angry that he tried and tried to think of a way to stop that church bell ringing, so that he could move back to the cosy hut.

One day his chance came. He was sitting on a tree stump beside the road which led to the valley, when a stranger passed by.

"Good morning," said the Troll.

"It's going to be another warm day. Are you going far?"

"Yes," said the man. "I'm going to the village of Jelling, where my sister Josie lives. Perhaps you can show me the way."

Now this was the village with the church.

"Well, you are on the right road," said the Troll. "You go straight over the hills and Jelling is in the second valley."

Then he remembered the church bell and saw his chance to get his own back.

"You can't miss it," he said. "There's a wooden church with a bell. But it's a long road and the day is warm. Would you like to come in for a drink?"

Now it's never a good idea to accept an invitation from a Troll. But would you know a troll if you met one? They're not at all easy to recog-

nise. Trolls look very much like ordinary people except for the wicked look deep in their eyes, and it's not easy to see that because of their thick bushy eyebrows.

So the traveller agreed.

"It's very kind of you to offer," he said, following the Troll into the cave.

"Oh yes," said the Troll. "I know that village well. In fact I have friends there. I wonder, would you take a letter to them for me?"

"Of course I'll deliver your letter," said the man. "It's little enough to do in return for a cool drink."

The man drank the cup of apple-juice that the Troll had given him. He found it rather bitter, but he was very thirsty.

Meanwhile the Troll went to the back of his cave and prepared a letter. He folded some paper and sealed it with blue wax. He wrote some words on the front. There were no words inside because this was a Troll-cup! It was full of magic!

"That's a funny-shaped letter!" thought the man when the Troll came back but he didn't get a chance to look at it closely because the Troll put it straight into his pocket.

"Now don't take it out until you reach the church," said the Troll with a wicked smile. "Then just toss it over the churchyard wall. My friends will collect it from there."

The man thought it was rather a strange thing to do but he agreed and went on his way. He climbed the road over the hill and down through the next valley. By the time he had climbed the next hill he was very tired, so he rested on a rock by the hillside and looked back across the valley.

"What a strange little man that was," he thought. "I wonder what sort of friends he has in Jelling." He remembered the letter in his pocket. He knew it was not polite to open other people's letters. "Perhaps I'll just peep at the address. Perhaps I know their name."

111

He took the letter from his pocket. As he held it, trying to make out the strange writing on the front, water started to drip from the corner. Then the letter began to swell up. It became fatter and fatter! As the pressure broke the magic wax it burst open letting a stream of water pour out, splattering the man's shoes. For as you know it wasn't a letter at all but a Troll-cup, full of water-magic!

Faster and faster flowed the water splashing on the grass, spreading out over the field and pouring down the hill. Soon the meadows at the bottom of the valley were flooded and still the water flowed. For the wicked Troll had put a whole lake inside the Troll-cup, hoping to fill the other valley, drowning the village of Jelling, its church, the steeple and the ringing bell.

When he saw what he had done the man was very frightened. He saw the water rising towards him. Birds flew up from the reeds, their nests floating on the swirling current. Rabbits hopped and sheep ran up the hill away from the quickly growing lake. Luckily, a small stream which wound down the hill was able to turn into a river and take the water away to the sea before it reached the top of the hill.

The poor man ran as fast as he could away from the new lake and did not stop until he came to the village and the church.

He sank down, panting against the wall of the churchyard. His sister came running from her house.

"Hans, Hans!" she cried, (for that was his name). "Why were you running so fast? Is the wild bull chasing you?"

"Oh, no, sister Josie," (for that was her name). "What a strange piece of luck. If I had not been a little nosey ... what a dreadful thing ... you and all your friends ... the whole valley ... drowned at the bottom of a lake ..."

"What are you babbling about?" said his sister. "Have you been touched by the sun? There is no lake near here."

"There is now," sighed Hans. "And all the water came from one little letter."

"A letter? How could a letter hold so much water?"

"Magic! Troll's magic," said Hans. "It must be. The man who gave it to me must have been a Troll."

The people of the village thought he was mad. In fact he had to take them all back over the hill to see the lake before they would believe him. They looked in amazement at the great new lake.

"I suppose it must be true," said sister Josie. "Seeing is believing."'

'Is that a true story?' asked Craig. 'Did he really make a new lake?'

'Well, there is a lake there,' said the Artist. 'Look at this picture postcard. One of my friends sent it from Denmark.'

Craig looked at the card then passed it to Lorna.

'As sister Josie said "Seeing is believing,"' said the Artist. 'Though I must admit I've never seen a Troll, have you? Now what about some Origami?'

Water Tricks – saving air and water

WATER SPIDER makes its own diving bell. It spins a thimble-shaped bell of silk fixed to water plants.

WILD TEASEL

The spider takes air down to fill the bell and stays inside during the day. It darts out to catch passing insects on the surface or in the water.

Stem leaves grow in pairs joined to form a large cup holding up to half a pint of rain water.

Insects are drowned and turn the liquid into a nourishing soup!

WATER HOLDING FROG
During dry spells, this Australian frog stays underground in a damp place, full of water, and inside its own cast-off skin.
   When the rain comes it digs itself out and feeds, breeds and the tadpoles grow very quickly into frogs. They fill up with water and bury themselves before the next dry spell.

Hunting Shooting and Fishing

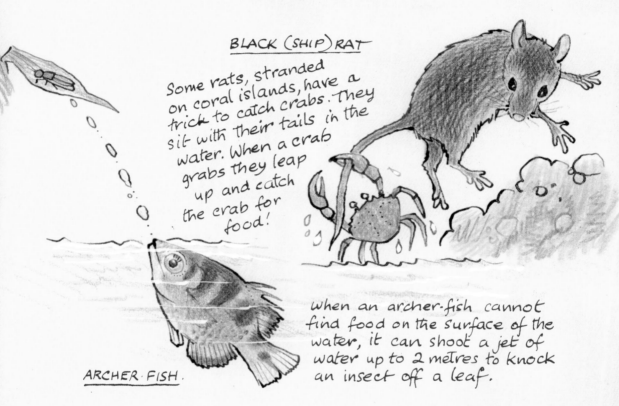

BLACK (SHIP) RAT

Some rats, stranded on coral islands, have a trick to catch crabs. They sit with their tails in the water. When a crab grabs they leap up and catch the crab for food!

ARCHER FISH.

When an archer-fish cannot find food on the surface of the water, it can shoot a jet of water up to 2 metres to knock an insect off a leaf.

THE DIPPER

The dipper flits about the rocks in fast flowing streams. They feed on various water-creatures. To catch these they can run into the water and "fly" submerged, using their wings and paddling with their feet.

Feathers very oily and waterproof.

Flaps to close the nostrils.

The Octopus   a water trick

TOOLS: MATERIALS : An egg. A curtain ring. Tissue or thin cloth. clingfilm.
SPOON. SCISSORS. Large glass jar. Waterproof glue. Large balloon or rubber glove.

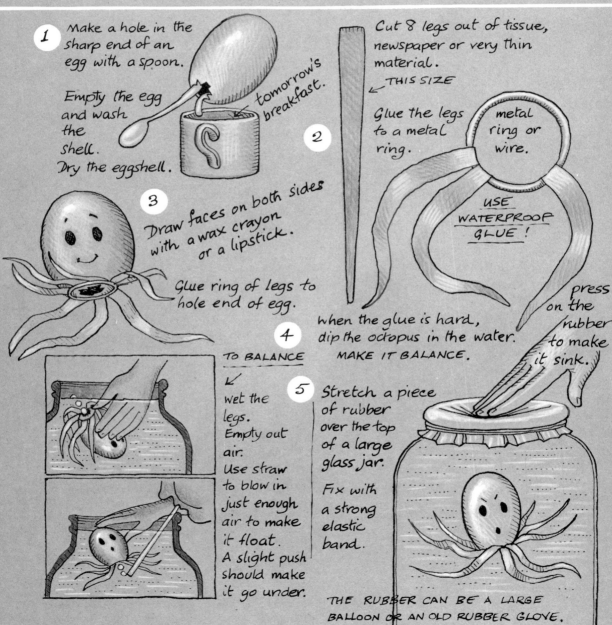

1. Make a hole in the sharp end of an egg with a spoon.

Empty the egg and wash the shell. Dry the eggshell.

tomorrow's breakfast.

2. Cut 8 legs out of tissue, newspaper or very thin material.

THIS SIZE

Glue the legs to a metal ring.

metal ring or wire.

USE WATERPROOF GLUE !

3. Draw faces on both sides with a wax crayon or a lipstick.

Glue ring of legs to hole end of egg.

When the glue is hard, dip the octopus in the water. MAKE IT BALANCE.

press on the rubber to make it sink.

4. TO BALANCE

Wet the legs. Empty out air. Use straw to blow in just enough air to make it float. A slight push should make it go under.

5. Stretch a piece of rubber over the top of a large glass jar.

Fix with a strong elastic band.

THE RUBBER CAN BE A LARGE BALLOON OR AN OLD RUBBER GLOVE.
it works better if you use clingfilm first.

A Paper Cup — a little origami

a square of strong paper 15cm. 2 paper clips.

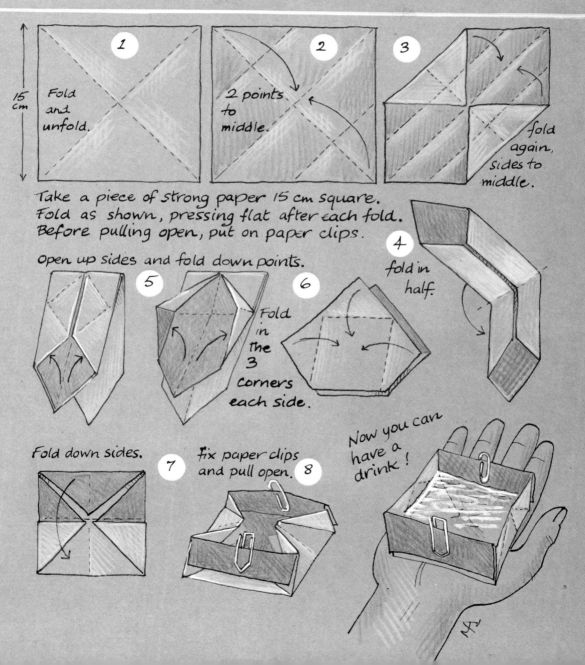

15 cm

1 Fold and unfold.

2 2 points to middle.

3 fold again, sides to middle.

Take a piece of strong paper 15 cm square.
Fold as shown, pressing flat after each fold.
Before pulling open, put on paper clips.

Open up sides and fold down points.

4 fold in half.

5

6 Fold in the 3 corners each side.

Fold down sides.

7 fix paper clips and pull open.

8 Now you can have a drink!

a Simple Troll from an old sock

TOOLS: Scissors. Needle.

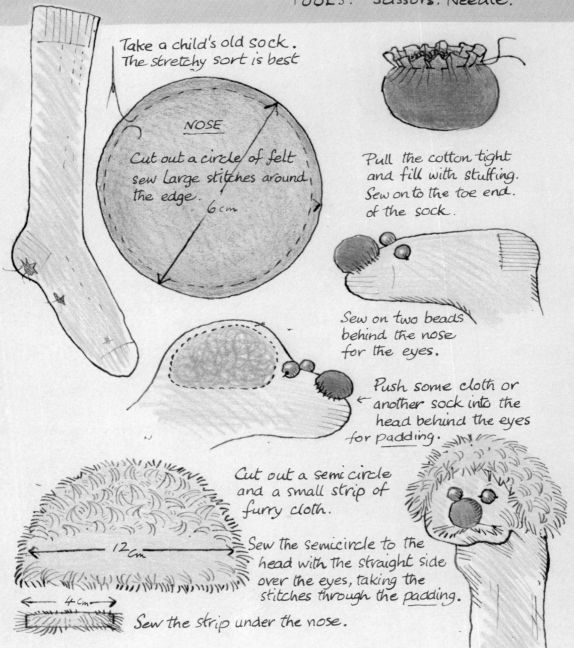

Take a child's old sock.
The stretchy sort is best

NOSE

Cut out a circle of felt
sew large stitches around
the edge. 6 cm

Pull the cotton tight
and fill with stuffing.
Sew on to the toe end.
of the sock.

Sew on two beads
behind the nose
for the eyes.

Push some cloth or
← another sock into the
head behind the eyes
for padding.

Cut out a semicircle
and a small strip of
furry cloth.

12 cm

4 cm

Sew the semicircle to the
head with the straight side
over the eyes, taking the
stitches through the padding.

Sew the strip under the nose.

MATERIALS: An old sock. Pieces of felt in four colours. Small piece of furry material. Cotton. Buttons, beads, buckles.

Make up the HAT out of these pieces of brown felt. Sew it on to the hair.

14 cm

2

4 cm
9 cm
CROWN
BRIM

Cut out jacket and wrap it round body. Sew into place with your hand in sock

6 cm

18 cm

9 cm

Cut the four pieces for arms and legs. Sew into tubes and stuff.
Make feet in the same way as nose. Stuff and sew on to legs. Cut out hands. Fold and sew. Stuff and sew to arms. Sew arms and legs in place.
Add collar, buttons, buckles, or anything else to brighten up the clothes.

10 cm
LEGS. cut two
5 cm

4
ARMS cut two
4 cm

Hands cut two
3 cm
4

This is how your hand fits

SIT HIM ON THE BACK OF A CHAIR AND SEE WHAT FUNNY FACES YOU CAN MAKE!

10. Bedtime Story

Do you know what "nocturnal" means? I'll tell you. Some animals and birds sleep at night – like you and me – and the dog – and the chickens.

But quite a lot of creatures sleep all day and only wake up when it is dark. They are called nocturnal creatures because they live their lives and do their hunting and feeding in the night. It's either safer for them in the dark, like hedgehogs and foxes, when humans are asleep. Or that's the best time to catch their food, like bats who flit about at night catching moths and flies, or owls whose feathers are so soft that they fly silently around listening for the mice rustling and squeaking.

The badger is nocturnal.

Most of the day he spends sleeping in his 'set'. At night he snuffles around in the starlight where his black and white stripes mix with the shadows so that he can hardly be seen at all.

Billy hoped to see a badger. But the trouble is, little boys are not nocturnal. He meant to rest on the garden seat for a few minutes until the moon came up, then he would start badger-watching.

But he fell asleep. That's where the Artist found him early in the morning.

'Why, it's Billy,' said the Artist, shaking him awake. 'Whatever are you doing out here? Why aren't you at home in bed?

'Where am I?' murmured Billy, drowsily. 'I'm cold.'

'I should think you are,' said the Artist. 'You're covered in dew. Does your mother know where you are?'

'Now I remember,' said Billy, waking up. 'I've been badger-watching.

See, I've got my binoculars and my soup. Mum knows where I am. Trouble is, I fell asleep. I only meant to have forty winks.'

'You had a few more winks than forty,' laughed the Artist. 'You'd better come in and warm yourself up.'

He unlocked his studio and they went in. Soon the stove was raked out and a good fire was burning.

'I'll find you a warm dry blanket somewhere,' said the Artist. 'If you wrap yourself up and sit in the big armchair you'll soon warm up.'

Soon the room was warm, Billy drank his soup and watched the Artist working.

'I feel a lot better now,' said Billy. 'Quite warm. And a bit drowsy. I don't think I slept very well on your garden seat.'

'I don't suppose it is very comfortable,' said the Artist. 'Although I can't say I've ever tried it – I prefer my bed.'

'This armchair is comfortable,' said Billy. 'I think I could sleep here.'

'You're welcome,' said the Artist. 'I can let your mum know where you are.'

'Thanks,' said Billy.' I don't suppose you could tell me a story – you know, a sort of sleepy one – a bedtime story?'

'Well, just a short one,' said the Artist.

So he told Billy a story about a big soft bed.

'Once upon a time,' he began, 'there were three bears . . .'

'I know that one,' interrupted Billy.

'This isn't the same story,' said the Artist. 'They lived in a great big rambling house on the posh side of the forest . . .'

'But they didn't,' said Billy. 'It was a little wooden house!'

'I'll never finish the story if you interrupt! They moved out of the little wooden hut when they became rich. I know all about Goldilocks and the Three Bears. In fact that's how they made their money. That story became so well-known that writers used it all the time in books and on television.

Old Father Bear saw all the writers driving around in their big cars and moving into big houses. He didn't see why they should be so rich when the bears themselves were poor, living in a wooden shack at the worst end of the forest with no main drains or running water.

So he got himself a lawyer who said: "We must take the case to court. Perhaps all these writers should have been paying you money."

So that's what they did. The Judge listened to their story. He looked at poor old Father Bear in his worn-out boots and shabby waist-coat and then at the writers who had come to hear the trial and he said:

"In future, any writer who uses your story will pay you fifty pence. It's what we call a royalty. They will pay you every time it is used, and what's more, they will pay NOW for all the times they have used your story in the past! You may need a large sack."

So Father Bear and Mother Bear borrowed a large cloth from the court cleaner and stood at the door as the writers went out. The writers tossed in their fifty pences as they passed and Baby Bear picked up any that missed. Soon the cloth was full and the Three Bears went home. The writers who hadn't come to court and those who were living abroad and all the French writers and German writers and writers from all the other countries where the story of the Three Bears had been used sent their fifty pences and their francs and their marks.

Soon Father Bear was rich enough to buy a big house and they moved in.

But I'm sorry to say their prosperity didn't last. The writers stopped using the Three Bears in their stories. They said they were old-fashioned and everyone wanted exciting spy stories now.

Poor old Father Bear!

The money was all spent before the bears had bought any furniture. There was only one thing to do. 'Do-it-yourself.'

But even that cost money. So Father Bear fetched fallen branches and pieces of trees that the woodmen had left lying around in the forest.

He made a table and three chairs.

A big one, a middle-sized one and a little one, of course, for Baby Bear. He cut up the wood with his blunt old saw and tied the bits together with pieces of string.

Well, one day, little Bill Badger lost his way in the woods. The path he followed led him to the front door of this big house.

He knocked on the door. Luckily the bears were in. They were having their tea.

"Come in," said Mother Bear. "Do have something to eat. It's just made."

She ladled porridge into an enormous wooden bowl.

"We used to have bread and butter and jam for tea," she said, "but since the bus fares went up we only get into town once a month and nothing keeps better than dry porridge oats."

She put the bowl of porridge on the table.

The table collapsed.

"I told you to use screws not string!" she said to Father Bear.

"Never mind," said Father Bear. "Have a chair and you can eat your porridge off your lap."

Billy sat on the smallest chair.

It seemed the polite thing to do.

The smallest chair fell to pieces.

"You might have known that would happen," said Baby Bear. "It always does."

"Sorry," said Billy. "I should have started with the biggest. I forgot."

He sat on the biggest chair of all, with his bowl of porridge on his lap. It slowly collapsed in a heap leaving Billy standing up.

So he tried the middle-sized one.

"That's my chair," smiled Mother Bear.

"I guessed it was," said Billy, as the back legs folded up. Billy fell over backwards spilling his porridge all over the floor.

"I made them myself," said Father Bear proudly.

"I thought so," said Billy. "Anyhow, I wasn't really hungry, but I am rather tired after my long walk."

"So am I," said Father Bear. "And I need some rest before doing any more woodwork. Let's all go to bed."

He led them up the stairs to the bedroom. Billy was surprised to see one enormous ricketty bed in the room.

"Did you make it yourself?" he asked politely.

"Oh no," said Father Bear. "I'm teaching Baby Bear to use his paws. He made it all by himself."

"How clever," said Billy. "But why so big?"

"Well," explained Baby Bear. "I really meant to make three beds. You know, a big one for Father Bear, a middle-sized one for Mother Bear, and a little one for me. But Father said I was too small to use the saw to cut the long pieces of wood."

"Oh yes," said Father Bear. "Safety First. Saws are too dangerous for Baby Bears."

"So, anyhow," said Baby Bear, "when I put the long pieces of wood together this is the size it turned out."

"Never mind," said Mother Bear. "It's plenty big enough for us all."

So the Three Bears and little Billy all climbed into the great big bed, cuddled up and fell fast asleep in the moonlight.'

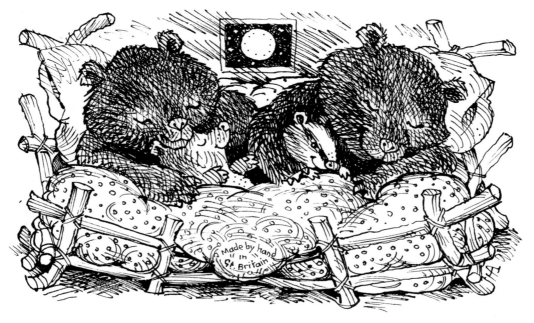

'There you are,' said the Artist. 'That was a real bedtime story.'

He looked down at Billy.

'Well don't you want to know whether the bed fell to pieces?'

But there was no answer. Billy was fast asleep too.

'Ah well,' he sighed, as he went out to post a fifty pence postal order to the Three Bears, 'it's a pity to disturb him. I'll telephone his mum while I'm at the post office.'

125

A Pop-up House *paper sculpture*

TOOLS: Scissors, Craft knife, blunt point.

1. Trace the 4 shapes on to thin card and cut out. Score the dotted lines for bending. Paint or colour.
2. Glue tabs A to end of other wall.
3. Glue 'inside walls' B together, keeping tabs C open.
4. Fold house flat so that inside wall is down and glue pictures to middle.

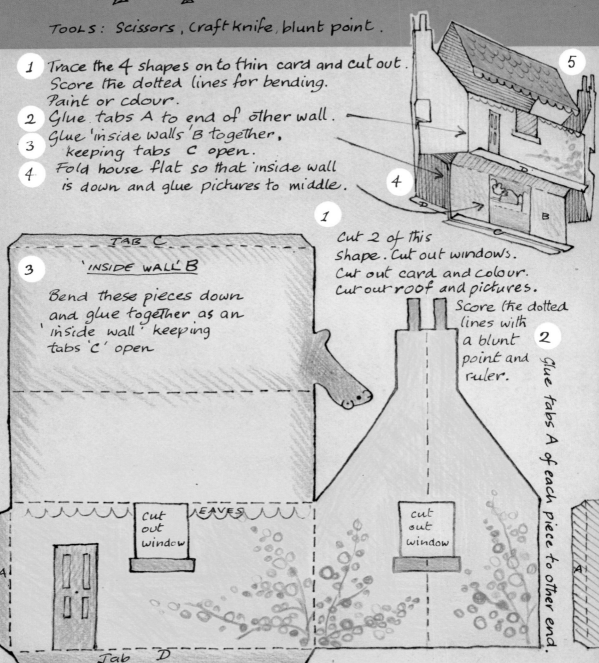

1 Cut 2 of this shape. Cut out windows. Cut out card and colour. Cut out roof and pictures.

2 Score the dotted lines with a blunt point and ruler.

Glue tabs A of each piece to other end.

TAB C

3 'INSIDE WALL' B

Bend these pieces down and glue together as an 'inside wall' keeping tabs 'C' open

EAVES

Cut out window

Cut out window

A

A

Tab D

Goldilocks and the Three Bears

MATERIALS: 2 pieces thin card   15 cm × 26 cm
          1 piece 9cm × 12cm   Glue. Paint or Crayons.

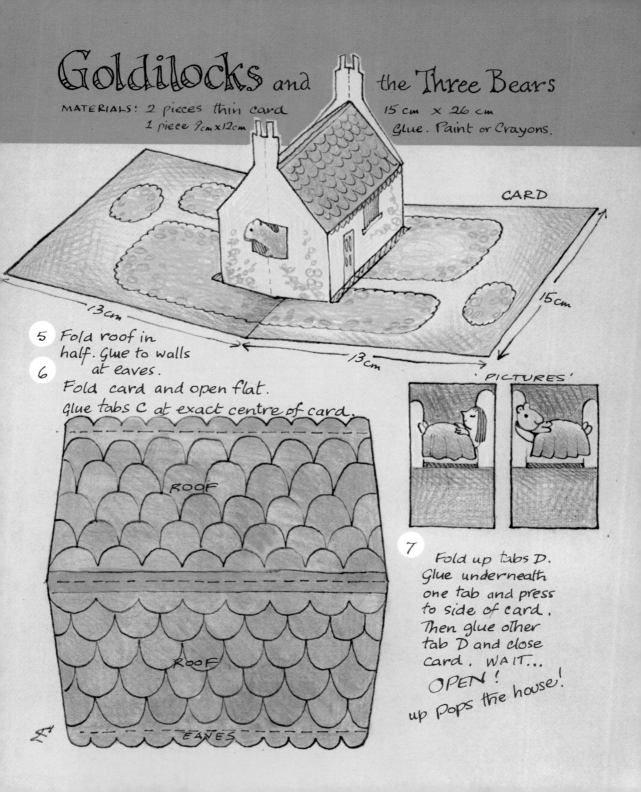

CARD

15 cm

13 cm

13 cm

5 Fold roof in half. Glue to walls at eaves.

6 Fold card and open flat. Glue tabs C at exact centre of card.

ROOF

ROOF

EAVES

'PICTURES'

7 Fold up tabs D. Glue underneath one tab and press to side of card. Then glue other tab D and close card. WAIT... OPEN! up Pops the house!

Sitting-Bear a sleeve-puppet

TOOLS: scissors, needle, pins, a sewing machine (if possible).

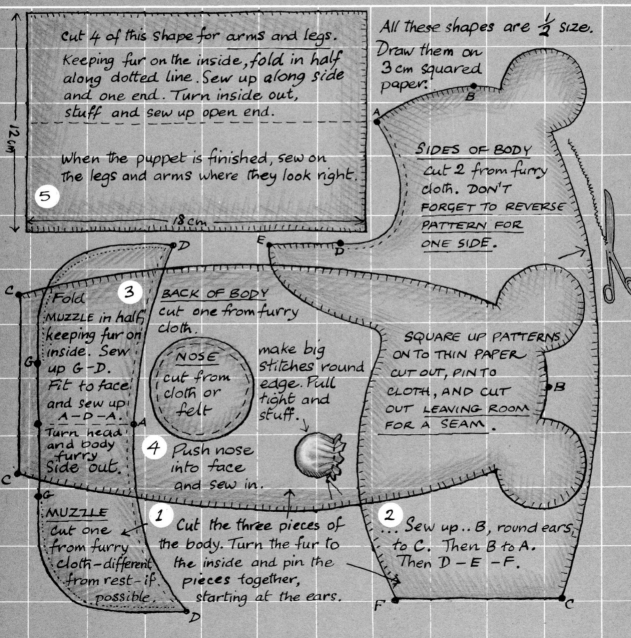

5 Cut 4 of this shape for arms and legs.

Keeping fur on the inside, fold in half along dotted line. Sew up along side and one end. Turn inside out, stuff and sew up open end.

When the puppet is finished, sew on the legs and arms where they look right.

12 cm

18 cm

All these shapes are ½ size. Draw them on 3 cm squared paper.

A   B

SIDES OF BODY
cut 2 from furry cloth. DON'T FORGET TO REVERSE PATTERN FOR ONE SIDE.

E   D

D

3 Fold MUZZLE in half, keeping fur on inside. Sew up G–D. Fit to face and sew up A–D–A. Turn head and body furry side out.

C

G

C

G

BACK OF BODY
cut one from furry cloth.

NOSE
cut from cloth or felt

make big stitches round edge. Pull tight and stuff.

A

SQUARE UP PATTERNS ON TO THIN PAPER CUT OUT, PIN TO CLOTH, AND CUT OUT LEAVING ROOM FOR A SEAM.

B

4 Push nose into face and sew in.

MUZZLE
cut one from furry cloth – different from rest – if possible.

D

1 Cut the three pieces of the body. Turn the fur to the inside and pin the pieces together, starting at the ears.

2 ... Sew up .. B, round ears, to C. Then B to A. Then D – E – F.

F   C

MATERIALS: A piece of furry material 45 cm x 45 cm. Stuffing.
A small piece of felt for nose. Cotton.
Buttons or teddy bear eyes.
An old worn-out jumper.

When the puppet is made, take an old worn-out jersey or buy one from a jumble-sale. Cut a hole half-way along the right sleeve and sew the puppet on. Sew an old glove to the sleeve and stuff the arm with cloth or paper.

Put on the jersey, and the other glove. Your right arm goes up into the puppet, and the dummy arm rests on the back of a chair.

EYES
If you have no teddy-bear eyes use buttons.

sew here

old jersey

glove

Dummy Arm

Stuff with cloth or newspaper

11. Low Cloud

It was early on Christmas morning. The Artist had arrived early at his studio. He fumbled in his pockets for the key and opened the door.

He fumbled because it was a very cold morning. He was wearing his thick duffel coat and the pockets weren't easy to find. What made it worse were the thick woolly mittens he was wearing and the thick scarf that his granny had knitted him. It hung down in front and got in his way.

A thick mist had risen from the river and the bushes were coated with frost.

Walter was waiting for him at the door.

'You're up early,' said the Artist. 'Has Father Christmas been?'

'Yes, I was awake as soon as it was light,' said Walter, 'I got a painting box – and a pad – and some brushes – um . . . – and a new red rain-hat . . . er, er, and new red wellies . . .'

'Well come in and show me,' said the Artist. 'But take off those muddy boots first.'

They went inside. Walter took off his new red wellies and left them by the door. He went over and sat in the Artist's big leather armchair. He reached inside his coat and brought out a pad of paper. He pulled a paintbox from his pocket with a smile and opened it to show the brushes.

He laid all his presents along the arms of the chair.

'There,' he said, proudly, 'now I can help you with your work.'

'So you can,' said the Artist, as he spread out a big sheet of paper on his drawing board. I could do with some help today.'

'But it's Christmas day,' said Walter. 'Don't you give yourself a holiday for Christmas?'

'Oh yes, I'll be home for my Christmas dinner, but I must paint just one picture first. I was hoping to go out and paint a landscape, but just look out there!'

Walter looked out of the big bow window.

'It's very foggy,' he said.

'More like low cloud,' said the Artist. 'I don't think I could see far enough this morning to paint my own nose.'

'Perhaps it will lift?' suggested Walter.

'My nose?'

'No,' giggled Walter. 'The low cloud. It usually does.'

'Usually,' agreed the Artist. 'Although I can remember one cloud that took some persuading.'

'How do you persuade a cloud? asked Walter, ''You can't talk to a cloud!'

'You can talk to anything,' corrected the Artist, 'but it may not always listen. If you really want to hear about it I'll tell you. Perhaps by the time I've finished, the cloud will have lifted.'

'Yes please,' said Walter.

'But keep looking out of that window,' said the Artist. 'I want to know when the mist has gone, I might get carried away and not notice.'

'Carried away?' said Walter. 'What do you mean?'

The Artist did not answer. He began the story:

'It was a lovely day in the wood. Big white clouds sailed fluffily across the sky. Down in the wood there wasn't a breath of wind.

The Coypu stood at the edge of the trees and sniffed the air.

"It's a good day for ... sniff-sniff ... for painting," he said.

"Good idea," said the Fox, leaning against an oak tree. "I'll join you."

"I didn't know you painted," said the Coypu. "Where are your paints?"

131

"Oh, I don't paint, not personally," said the Fox. "But I know a lot about it. I know all the rules. I'll come along to give you friendly advice and encouragement."

The Coypu put on his big painting hat and picked up his paint box and canvas.

"Well, if you've nothing better to do," he said, "I don't mind. It would be encouraging if you could carry my easel."

The Fox carried the easel and they set off out of the wood and across the meadow towards the cabbage field. On the way they passed a wooded bank. That's where the Badger lived. He popped his head out of his hole.

"What's happened?" he shouted. "Where are you going in such a hurry?"

"We're not in a hurry," answered the Coypu. "We're just going painting."

"Fainting?" repeated the Badger, who was rather deaf. "Who's fainting? Do you need help? First Aid?"

He noticed the folding easel that the Fox was carrying:

"Ah, good, I see you've got the stretcher, we might need that. I'll be along in two shakes."

They reached the edge of the cabbage field. The Coypu set up his canvas on the easel and opened the painting box.

The Fox peered into the box. He poked around among paper packets and bottles and brushes.

"There are only two tubes of paint here," he said. "You haven't got a full set of colours."

"How could I bring a full set in there," said the Coypu. "Do you realise how many colours there are? There's blue and red and yellow, and brown and purple and – and green and orange. There's crimson and puce and violet and mauve. There's Indian yellow and yellow ochre and brilliant yellow and lemon yellow and then there's all the blues. There's . . ."

"Yes, yes," interrupted the Fox, "but how can you paint landscapes with only two colours?"

"Well, you see," explained the Coypu, "After I'd put in my sandwiches and my bottle of lemonade there was only room for two tubes. Anyhow, there aren't only two colours, there's only one colour. It's green. The other tube is white and that's not a colour, so there!"

"Polychromatic paucity!" insisted the Owl, missing the easel and crashing down among the cabbages.

"Oh, it's all right," said the Coypu. "I told you. It's green! I only need green. I paint cabbages."

"Cabbages?" exclaimed the Fox. "Artists don't paint cabbages. They paint beautiful things."

"Well, I think cabbages are beautiful," said the Coypu, huffily.

"Succulent sauerkraut," hissed the Owl as he staggered out damply from the cabbage field.

"Oh, no," said the Fox. "Trees are beautiful and flowers; mountains and sunsets and clouds-in-the-sky. Those are the things that artists paint, old boy, not cabbages."

"Oh dear," sighed the Coypu, "I'm not sure that I could paint those things. They must be very difficult. I've only ever painted cabbages."

"But do people buy cabbage paintings?" asked the Fox. "Have you sold many?"

"Oh no, I've never sold a picture," said the Coypu.

"Well then, try a 'cloud-in-the-sky' for a start. Clouds are not too hard and they are very popular."

"But you know I've no blue paint for the sky," said the Coypu. "Skies are always blue."

"Then paint it green," said the Fox. "If you want the sky green, paint it green. It is allowed. That's what is called *self-expression*."

So the Coypu brushed green paint all around the edges of the canvas, leaving a dumpy shape in the middle for the cloud. He took a clean brush and swirled white paint onto the cloud.

"There, I've finished," he said. "What do you think?"

"Not bad at all," commented the Fox. In fact, it is quite good. Don't you think so, Owl?"

"Extraordinarily psychedelic," said the Owl, who as you will have guessed, was very fond of long words.

"Oh dear," said the Coot, arriving. "Whatever is it?"

"It's a *cloud-on-a-green-sky*," said the Coypu, proudly munching a cabbage leaf. "It's called *self-expression!*"

"Cumulo-nimbus," corrected the Owl, falling off the easel.

"Oh, how shocking! Such words!" sighed the Coot, fainting elegantly.

"Sorry I'm late," panted the Badger. "Where's the patient?"

"There they are," said the Fox, pointing to the two birds.

"Give them air," said the Badger. "Stand back!" He took a cabbage leaf from the Coypu and began to wave it over the birds.

"Artificial Respiration," murmured the Owl, recovering.

"Here!" protested the Coypu, "Stop waving my dinner about!" He tried to snatch back the cabbage leaf.

Well, they were so busy pointing and painting, and snatching and fainting, that they didn't notice the Cloud. Being an inquisitive cloud, it came down to see what all the fuss was about; just stopped sailing by and floated right down.

Then, catching sight of the painting, it wanted a closer look.

"Who's pushing?" said the Fox.

"Do keep back! Give them air!" said the Badger.

But the Cloud just hovered there nudging.

"It's the Cloud!" whispered the Coypu.

"So much for our sunny day!" said the Fox.

"How can artists be expected to paint 'clouds-in-the-sky'," said the Coypu, pointedly, "if the clouds won't stay in the sky."

The Cloud did not budge. The Coot sat up and blinked.

"Oh dear, where am I?" she asked. "There's a mist in front of my eyes."

"Not mist," said the Fox. "Low cloud."

"Making shadows and nudging," said the Coypu. "It's being a bit of a wet blanket."

"It just won't stand back," said the Badger.

"Obstinate evaporation," said the Owl.

"Have you asked it nicely?" said the Coot.

"I dropped a hint," said the Fox.

The Coot turned to the Cloud.

"Don't you think, Cloud, dear," she said sweetly, "you'd be far better off up there in the blue sky, sailing along with all the other pretty clouds? Of course, we simply love your company, although you make it just the teeniest bit dull, and Coypu's painting won't dry, and Owl's feathers are getting all wet. But, if a wind started to blow, you might get blown across the ploughed field. You wouldn't like to get your . . . er . . . underneath all muddy, would you?"

"Or blown into the woods," added the Coypu. "You might get spiked on a holly bush!"

"Or turned into smog in the town," said the Fox.

In the end, as all this talk didn't seem to have the slightest effect on the Cloud, the animals decided to try something different. They all took long sticks to LIFT the Cloud.

"Ready . . ." said the Fox. "Steady . . . LIFT!"

But of course, clouds are soft. The sticks went right through. In fact, the Cloud seemed to settle even lower, hiding the animals so that only their feet stuck out underneath.

"Insubstantial gasification!" grumbled the Owl, muffled.

"I've had an idea!" said the Fox, emerging. "I think the Cloud came down to see its picture!"

"Of course," said the Coypu. "I don't suppose it's ever had its portrait painted before."

"Well, then. If it is so interested in the picture, perhaps it would like to own it!"

"You mean, the Cloud could be my first customer?" said the Coypu.

"Yes, that is, if you would sell it."

"I'll give it away!" said the Coypu, delighted. "In fact I'll deliver it at once!"

So the picture was delivered and the Cloud went away at last, satisfied.'

'And that,' said the Artist, 'was how they got rid of their cloud. Has ours gone yet?'

'Oh, I forgot to say,' said Walter. 'Yes it's gone. But how did the Coypu deliver it?'

The Artist lifted up the picture he had been painting.

'Like this,' he said, as he put away his brushes. 'Now off you go. I don't think I'll need to paint a landscape after all. I'm going home for my Christmas dinner.'

The Artist

paste and paper heads

If you have plasticine you can make a head of any shape or even hands. If not, you can use a balloon, apple or carrot or anything that can be cut.

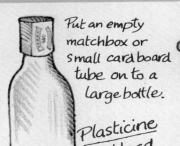

Put an empty matchbox or small cardboard tube on to a large bottle.

Plasticine Head

model the head on to the tube.

Make it about as big as a tangerine.

Cover with clingfilm.

MAKE PASTE (see back page)

Tear one sheet of a small newspaper into short strips. Lay out a few strips at a time, paste, and press on to the head.

Make the nose for the BALLOON head by rolling some pasted paper.

Use a stiff brush to press paper in.

If using fingers to smooth paper wet them under tap.

USE UP MOST OF THE PAPER! (about 8 layers) Leave overnight in a warm place 'til really dry.

be careful of sharp knives!

PLASTICINE HEAD

cut off back of head and dig out Plasticine.

Glue together and cover the join with pasted paper.

↑ 3 cm Trim edge to 3 cm. ↓

make large holes around the edge.

Paint the head pink or brown. Draw eyes and mouth.

Glue on cottonwool or stuffing for hair and

Whiskers.

BALLOON HEAD

Blow it up to the right size.

Tie it with string.

Cut a notch in the tube (matchbox).

Pull the string through and fix it in the notch.

WHEN DRY

prick the balloon and pull it out of the head.

SIZE AS
SHOWN

BODY. Make body as for Fox puppet.
Make LEGS and HANDS as for TROLL puppet.
Sew on to body. Make TROUSERS and slide on to
legs. Make and stuff BOOTS. Sew on to Legs.
SMOCK To make paper pattern, fold paper in half.
Trace this shape on it, with fold on left. OPEN out.
Pin to thin cloth and cut out.
SMOCKING Make 4 lines of stitches across

front as shown. Pull tight and tie
ends. Cut matching shape for back.

Centre-fold of paper pattern

Tack together with knots outside.
Ask mum to sew it on the machine.
Turn right side out.

SOLE OF BOOT
Cut 2

SIDE OF
BOOT

Cut 4.
sew sides together,
then sew on sole.

Sew here

Push body into
smock and sew at hands
and neck.
Push neck
tube into head.
Fix by
sewing to
holes in
neck.

Cover joins at neck
and hands by glueing
collar and cuffs.

Try a carrot or
potato!

Cut 2 this shape
for TROUSER LEGS.

MAKING PULLEYS. The best way to make pulleys for legs or wheels is to use one small disc of thick card and two larger discs of thin card. But it is easier to cut three discs of thin card with scissors for the smaller one. Glue them together. Make sure that the hole is big enough for a paper fastener to turn easily.

Ask mum or dad first!

MAKING PASTE
mix a heaped tablespoonful of flour, with a few drops of cold water until smooth in a china bowl.

Boil a cup of water, pour on to the paste, stirring.

Pour the paste back into the saucepan and heat until it thickens. Wait till it cools and use to paste paper.

Remember! many wallpaper pastes have fungicides which are poisonous. It's safer to use flour.

PERFORMING WITH PUPPETS.

If you have a clothes-horse make a theatre with some old curtains or cloth.

Use a chair in the corner of the room.